Mi-24 HIND
in action

By Hans-Heiri Stapfer

Color By Don Greer
Illustrated By Perry Manley

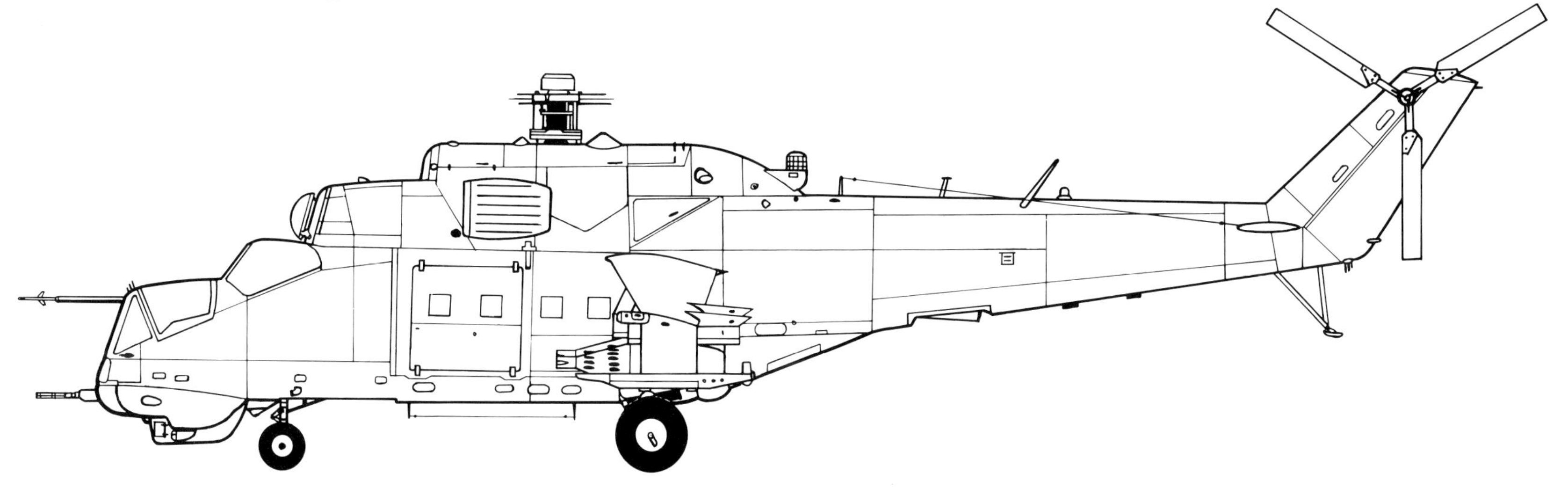

Aircraft Number 83

squadron/signal publications, inc.

A pair of Hind D gunships return from an airstrike against the *Mujahideen* in the rugged mountains of Afghanistan. Soviet and Afghan Hinds are widely used to provide air support, convoy escort, and to pursue escaping guerrillas.

ISBN 0-89747-203-9

If you have any photographs of the aircraft, armor, soldiers or ships of any nation, particularly wartime snapshots, why not share them with us and help make Squadron/Signal's books all the more interesting and complete in the future. Any photograph sent to us will be copied and the original returned. The donor will be fully credited for any photos used. Please send them to:

Squadron/Signal Publications, Inc.
1115 Crowley Drive.
Carrollton, TX 75011-5010.

DEDICATION

This book is respectfully dedicated to all beer drinkers.

Acknowledgements

This book would have been impossible without the assistance and co-operation of many institutions, organizations and individuals on both sides of the 'Gardenfence'. My thanks go to my friends Robert Bock, Walter Hodel, Robert J. Ruffle, Don Henry, C. M. Reed, and Peter Schneider, who provided me with information on Soviet helicopters and to the Swiss Military Library at Bern for their kind support. I owe a sincere "Thank You" to the following institutions and organizations:

Smithsonian Institution Library
P.Z.L. Swidnik
Aeroflot Office Zurich
Russian Aviation Research Group of Air Britain
Div Stutz of ASMZ
Aviaexport Moscow
Interflug-Industrieflug
US Department of the Air Force
Armeemuseum Dresden
Hannu and Rauni Valtonen of Keski-Suomen Ilmailumuseo

Articles from Eastern European magazines and books contained an unexpected amount of information on Soviet helicopters. Information from the following magazines proved to be very useful for research:

Aviazija I Kosmonautika
Modellist Konstruktor (Soviet Union)
Skrzydlata Polska
Flieger Revue
Volksarmee
Krylja Rodiny
L+K (Czechoslovakia)
Zolnierz Polski (Poland)
Armee Rundschau
(German Democratic Republic)

I apologize to anyone that I may have forgotten and last but not least I would like to take this opportunity to thank Nick 'The Old Man' Waters III for editing my English into American and for allowing me the extra eight pages needed to make this a more complete and accurate book on the Hind. If my bookkeeping is accurate, it took exactly 124 bottles of beer as well as two bottles of Vodka and two bottles of Swiss Kirschwater to complete this book; my thanks to Brew Masters around the world.

Photo Credits

Interflug-Industrieflug
Bob Bock
Javier Goto
Don Henry
Hans Reichle
Nicholas J. Waters III
Polish Air Force
Martin Bowman
Urs Harnisch
Walter Hodel
Robert J. Ruffle
Aeroflot Office Zurich
Fred Feuerstein
I.F.A. Photo Service
R.J. Howard
Markus Steiner

The Mil Mi-24 Hind E assault helicopter armed with a gatling gun, rockets, and four AT-6 Spiral anti-tank missiles has gained a notorious reputation in the West. The Hind has seen combat in Afghanistan, Angola, and Nicaragua and is very effective in the ground support role.

10

INTRODUCTION

The Mil Mi-24 Hind*, has become one of the most widely known assault helicopter gunships in the world. The Hind's impressive firepower and the vast numbers available to the Warsaw Pact are of major concern to NATO planners. The Hind forms the backbone of first line assault helicopter regiments in every Warsaw Pact nation. In the event of war NATO planners estimate Allied forces would encounter hundreds of Hinds over European front lines in the opening stages of a Warsaw Pact armored assault.

The Hind's roots can be traced back to the late 1950s, when the Soviet government issued a requirement for a new transport helicopter to replace the aging Mil Mi-4 Hound. This helicopter was to emerge as the Mi-8 Hip, entering service first with Aeroflot (the Soviet state airline) and later the Soviet Air Force. The Mi-8 Hip was originally designed as a medium lift transport helicopter, however, the aircraft was modified to fill a number of specialized roles, including that of a heavily armed gunship. Mi-8 components were later used as the basis for the Mil Mi-24 Hind, the first dedicated attack helicopter built in the Soviet Union.

The Mi-24 Hind is the Soviets answer to American helicopter gunships such as the Bell AH-1 Huey Cobra and McDonnell-Douglas AH-64 Apache. The Soviets, however, rejected the pure gunship concept popular in the West and designed a new class of helicopter — the assault helicopter. Assault helicopters are capable of both carrying troops into battle and supporting them with devastating firepower. There is currently no western equivalent to the assault helicopter.

Mikhail L. Mil, the Soviet Union's most prominent designer of rotary winged aircraft. Mil's designs include the Mi-1 Hare, Mi-4 Hound, Mi-6 Hook and Mi-8 Hip. Mil died of cancer on 31 December 1970 too early to see the success of his design bureau's latest creation, the Mil Mi-24 Hind.

Mikhail L. Mil

Mikhail Leontevich Mil was born on 9 November 1909 in the Soviet city of Irkutsk. In 1926 he entered the Siberian Technological Institute at Tomsk, and later studied at the Aviation Institute in Novotsherkask. In 1929 he helped design the first Soviet autogiro, the KaSKR-1, under the guidance of N.I. Kamov and I.K. Skrishinsky.

Mil graduated from the Novotsherkask Institute in 1931 and joined the Autogiro and Helicopter Department of the Central Aero and Hydrodynamic Institute (TsAGI) in Moscow where he was engaged in research on helicopter aerodynamics. By 1936 he had become an engineer in the helicopter design bureau and later became deputy to the Chief-Designer, Nikolai Kamov.

After the start of the Great Patriotic War (World War II) Mil was appointed Senior Engineer of the First Autogiro Artillery Communications Squadron at Smolensk. This unit was equipped with five TsAGI A-7bis autogiros and flew night operations until deactivated in October of 1941. Two years later Mil returned to the Central Aero and Hydrodynamic Institute and joined the Communist Party of the Soviet Union. During his wartime service he used his engineering background to design improved control systems for the Il-2 *Stormovick* ground attack aircraft and the Il-4 twin engined bomber.

In 1945 Mil received his Doctorate of Technology and by 1947 he had become the Chief Designer of a newly created helicopter experimental design bureau. Over the coming years his helicopter design bureau (helicopter OKB) designed a number of helicopters which set world records for helicopter performance.

Mikhail Mil was much more than a designer and engineer, he was also an excellent pianist and artist. Mil's designs are a mixture of exact mathematic calculations and creative genius. His helicopter designs are said to be born in his sculptor's studio rather than on an engineer's drawing board. His credo as a helicopter designer and Soviet Patriot was simply put: *"I would like to build helicopters that help people, accelerate technical progress, and strengthen the Socialist economy. I also want to build helicopters that can defend my native country."*

Mil's achievements as a helicopter designer were recognized by a grateful nation and he was awarded the Order of Lenin, Order of the Great Patriotic War, Order of the Red Banner, and the Red Star. In 1966 he received the highest Soviet civilian award, Hero of Socialist Labor.

Mikhail L. Mil died from cancer in Moscow on 31 January 1970. His design bureau was taken over by Marat Tishchenko (designer of the Hind), however, Mil's name will always be associated with the birth, growing pains, and maturity of the Soviet helicopter industry.

**The names commonly associated with Soviet aircraft and helicopters in the West are not Russian names, but rather those assigned by NATO. To facilitate quick and accurate reporting of Soviet aircraft types, the NATO Air Standards Coordinating Committee assigns a name to each aircraft. Each name has a distinctive sound and also identifies the basic mission of the aircraft. Bombers are all given names beginning with 'B', fighters with 'F', transports with 'C', helicopters 'H' and miscellaneous aircraft are coded with names beginning with 'M'. Additionally propeller driven aircraft carry single syllable names while jet aircraft have multi-syllable names (helicopter names make no distinction between piston and turbine powerplants). Thus the code name Crate (IL-14) indicates a propeller driven transport, while Fishbed (MiG-21) indicates a jet fighter. Variants within a basic design are indicated by a letter suffix, i.e. Hind A through Hind F for the various variants of the Mi-24.*

Mi-1 Hare

In December of 1947 the Mil Design Bureau (MIL OKB) began development of a light helicopter under the designation GM-1.The prototype made its first flight, with test pilot M.K. Baikalov at the controls, in September of 1948. The GM-1 was powered by a 575 hp Ivchenko AI-26V engine and could carry three passengers. The GM-1 prototype successfully completed testing and was ordered into production under the designation Mi-1. When the aircraft was introduced into Soviet Air Force service NATO assigned it the code name Hare.

The fuselage of the Mi-1 is of tubular steel construction with stressed metal skin and an all metal semi-monocoque tail boom. The rotor blades were made of wood reinforced by a three section tapered tubular steel spar. The Mi-1 gave the Soviets a helicopter with performance equal to or superior to its Western counterparts. The Hare could carry a heavier load faster and higher than its American counterpart, the Sikorsky S-51.

A number of variants of the basic Mi-1 were built. The Mil Mi-1U was a training variant with dual controls. The Mi-1S ambulance carried two gondolas on each side of the fuselage for stretchers. The Mi-1NKh was an agricultural variant used for crop dusting, equipped with spray bars on both sides of the fuselage and chemical tanks capable of holding a total of 500 liters of chemicals. The final production variant of the Hare, the Mi-1 *Moskvich*, was developed in 1961 and featured all metal rotor blades, better sound proofing, hydraulic controls, and improved instrumentation. During the early 1960s trials were conducted with armed variants of the Hare. Anti-tank missile pylons were fitted on both sides of the fuselage, however, the armed Mi-1 was less than successful and was not put into production. Production of the Mi-1 was phased out in the Soviet Union and all jigs and tools were transferred to Poland during 1954. Over 1,700 Mi-1s have been built at the P.Z.L. Factory at Swidnik near Lublin.

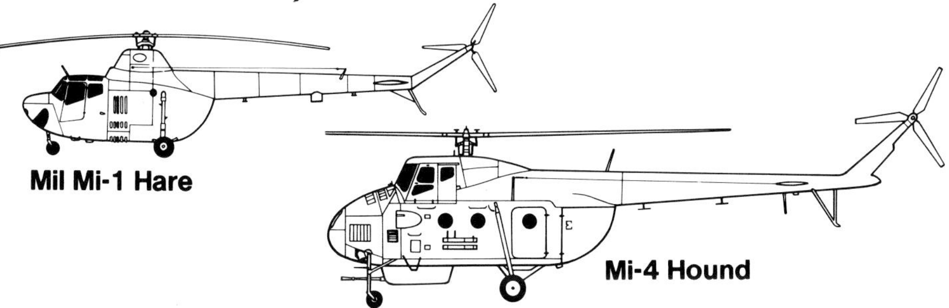

The Mi-1 Hare was the first Soviet helicopter put into large scale production. This late production Mi-1M (Moskvich) of the para-military DOSAAF — the Voluntary Society for Assistance to the Army, Air Force and Navy was built in Poland.

Mi-4 Hound

In mid-1951 Joseph Stalin ordered the Soviet helicopter industry to design a twelve passenger helicopter suitable for both civil and military use. He set a strict deadline — one year to design, build, and test fly a prototype. The Mil OKB undertook the project with initial design work beginning in October of 1951. In April of 1952 the first pre-production aircraft (there was no prototype as such) was completed — seven months after Stalin's order.

Powered by an 1,100 hp Shvetsov ASH-62IR radial engine mounted in the nose the helicopter made its first flight a month later with V. Vinitsky at the controls. The first pre-production aircraft had a gross weight of 17,196 pounds, three times larger than the Mi-1. State acceptance trials were successful and during the Summer of 1952 the helicopter was ordered into production under the designation Mi-4. Production Mi-4s were powered by a 1,700 hp ASH-82V engine instead of the 1,100 hp ASH-62IR engine of the pre-production aircraft.

As production increased a number of improvements were made to the Mi-4. The fuselage was reinforced to carry heavier cargos and the rotor blades were redesigned to overcome the blade's tendency to droop and almost strike the airframe. The Mi-4 was publicly shown for the first time at the 1953 Tushino Air Show and shortly afterwards NATO christened the new Soviet helicopter the Hound. In April of 1956 a modified Mi-4 was used to set three world records for helicopter performance.

Mi-4s were developed for both civil and military tasks. The Mi-4P was a ten passenger commercial variant, a Salon variant with accommodation for six passengers in a plush cabin was offered, and an agricultural variant, the Mi-4S, was equipped with a 1,450 liter tank in the fuselage and spray bars on each side of the fuselage.

The military Hound A transport could carry eight to sixteen troops or a jeep sized vehicle. The Mi-4MA Hound B anti-submarine warfare (ASW) variant carried a surface search radar under the nose and MAD gear on the rear fuselage. The Hound C was an airborne communications relay aircraft equipped with multiple receiver and transmitter antennas. Besides being used for military missions Hound Cs were used as radio/TV relay stations for Soviet sporting events.

Transport Hound As were fitted with a single TKB-481 12.7MM machine gun fired by the flight engineer from a gondola under the fuselage. The Soviets used armed Hounds to test and refine vertical assault helicopter tactics. During these early trials a number of Mi-4s were equipped with outrigger pylons on each side of the fuselage for UB-16 rocket pods or anti-tank missiles. The Hound proved unsuitable as a gunship and the armament system was not used operationally, however, the outrigger weapons mounts set the pattern for future Soviet armed helicopters.

An Mi-4 (CCCP-38300) of Aeroflot (Soviet state airline) lands an inspection team on a ranch in Russia. The Hound is Light Gray with a Red cockpit and upper tail boom. The civil registration and Aeroflot logo are in Black. The Hound was the standard Soviet transport helicopter in the late 1950s and early 1960s.

Development

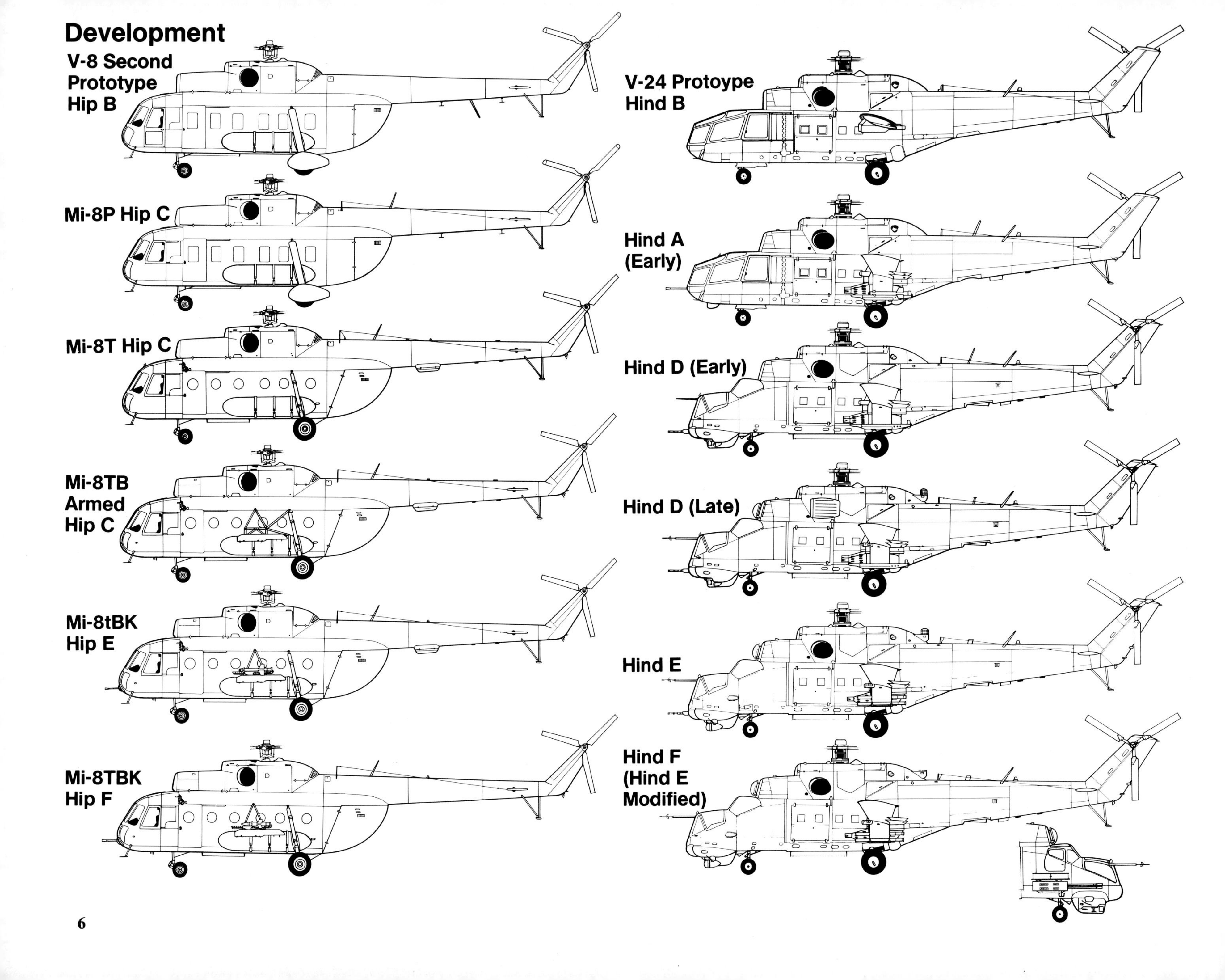

V-8 (Mi-8) Prototypes

In 1958 the Mil OKB began development of replacements for the highly reliable Mi-1 and Mi-4 series of helicopters. Turbine engines designed specifically for helicopters had become available which offered a number of advantages over the piston engines used in the earlier Mi-1 and Mi-4. The turbine engines were lighter, smaller, and used inexpensive jet fuel instead of expensive high octane gasoline. These advantages led to a decision to replace both the Mi-1 and Mi-4 with new designs of nearly equal size but powered by turbine engines. The Mi-2 Hoplite was the successor to the Mi-1. After production and testing of two prototypes in the Soviet Union, production of the Mi-2 was transferred to Poland where the first Polish-built Mi-2 flew on 4 November 1965.

To replace the Mi-4 Mil proposed a twenty-eight passenger medium lift transport helicopter under the designation V-8*. The V-8 prototype was a conventional all metal fuselage pod and tail boom helicopter eighty-three feet long (four feet six inches longer than the Mi-4) with an internal cabin volume some 45 percent greater than the Mi-4, increasing usable payload by over 4,000 pounds.

In an effort to reduce development time the rotor hub, rotor and tail boom from an Mi-4 were fitted to the first V-8 prototype. The prototype was powered by a single 2,700 shp (shaft horse power) AI-24V turbine engine** mounted on the upper fuselage above the main cabin. The cockpit was located in the forward portion of the fuselage with side by side seating for the two pilots and provision for a flight engineer's seat mounted between and slightly behind the pilots. Two cockpit doors were installed on either side of the fuselage. Access to main cabin from the cockpit was through a door in the main fuselage bulkhead. The main cabin could hold twenty-four passengers or 8,820 pounds of cargo and was fitted with both a main cabin door on the port side of the fuselage and rear fuselage clamshell cargo doors.

The prototype's fuel system included an internal fuselage tank with a capacity of 254 gallons of jet fuel and provision for two external strap-on tanks. The starboard strap-on tank has a capacity of 388 gallons while the port tank holds 426 gallons. To increase endurance a 521 gallon auxiliary fuel tank can be carried in the cargo compartment. The fuel tanks, engines, reduction gear, and cabin heaters are equipped with automatic fire fighting systems.

The non-retractable tricycle landing gear has a steerable twin wheeled nose mount and low pressure single wheeled main mounts with streamlined wheel covers. The main landing gear is attached to the fuselage underside by two faired 'V' struts with a pneumatic shock strut running from the main mount to the upper fuselage side. A fixed and braced shock absorbing tail skid is installed under the rear of the tail boom.

The prototype V-8 was unveiled to the public at the Tushino Air Show on 9 July 1961. NATO Military Attaches attending the show quickly reported the existence of the new Soviet helicopter and this prototype was assigned the NATO code name Hip A.

To improve the prototypes reliability and flight safety it was decided that the single 2,700 shp engine of the first prototype would be replaced by a pair of coupled 1,500 shp Izotov TV-2-117 turboshaft engines mounted side by side on the second prototype. The second prototype also had newly designed all metal constant chord rotor blades, and a VHF radio blade antenna was installed under the tail boom. The second V-8 prototype flew for the first time on 17 September 1962 with Mil test pilot Koloshenko at the controls. The pilot reported that the prototype handled very well throughout the flight envelope, there was almost no vibration, and cockpit noise levels were greatly improved over earlier helicopters. This prototype was given the NATO code Hip B.

**New Mil designs are usually designated 'V', for Vertoljot (Helicopter), during the design and experimental stage. When the aircraft goes into production the designation is changed to 'Mi' denoting a production helicopter of the Mil OKB.*

***The AI-24V turbine engine was developed by Pavel A. Solovjov, the deputy chief designer of the Shvetsov engine design bureau. Solovjov later became head of the design bureau developing a series of powerplants that were used on other well known Soviet aircraft such as the Mi-6, Mi-10, Tu-134, Il-62 and Il-76.*

The first V-8 prototype used the rotor head, rotor blades, and tail boom from an Mi-4 Hound. The prototype was powered by a single 2,700 shp AI-24V turbine engine.

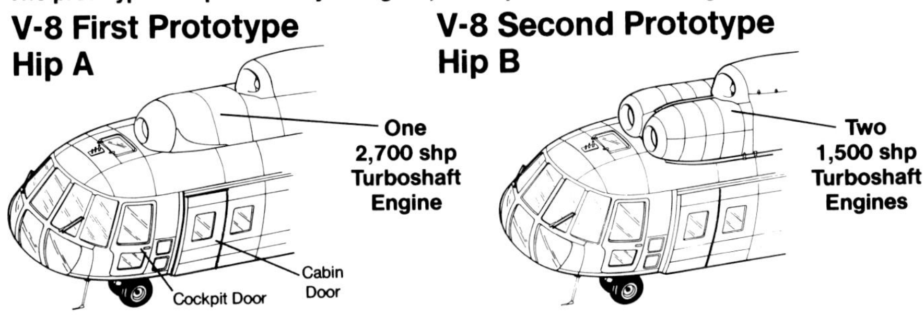

The second V-8 Hip prototype was powered by two 1,500 shp Izotov TV-2-117 turboshaft engines instead of the single 2,700 shp Solovjov turbine of the first prototype. The prototype flew for the first time on 17 September 1962 with a four blade main rotor adopted from the Mi-4 Hound.

Mi-8 Hip

State acceptance trials revealed that a number of changes and improvements were needed before the V-8 could go into production at Kazan and Ulan-Ude. The prototype's four blade rotor system was replaced by a five blade rotor, the cockpit doors were deleted, the VHF radio antenna was relocated to the top of the tail boom, the windows were enlarged, a framed two piece nose cockpit window replaced the smaller single unframed panel, and the windscreen wiper blades were repositioned. Once these changes were incorporated, the V-8 was ordered into production under the designation Mi-8.

Production Mi-8s are powered by two 1,500 shp TV-2-117A turbine engines which are governed by a unique automatic power regulating system. The system regulates engine power through the transmission to the main rotor, governing engine rpm's and guaranteeing equal power from each engine. In the event an engine loses power or fails, the system automatically increases power from the remaining engine. Additionally, the engine controls are equipped with a manual backup system which allows the crew to manually control engine power and rpms.

The main rotor system is equipped with hydraulic dampers that lessen the effects of ground resonance (vibration) during takeoff, landings, and in a hover. The main rotor consists of five rectangular blades consisting of an aluminum spar and leading edge with honeycomb filled, metal skinned rear sections fastened to the main spar. The main spar is gas pressurized with a loss of pressure warning system that sounds an alarm in case of damage to the blade spar. Both the main and three blade tail rotor are equipped with electrothermal deicing equipment to prevent ice build up on the blades.

Electronics installed on the Mi-8 included: ARK-U2 radio compass, R-860 command radio, RW-3 radio altimeter, ARK-9 radio compass, R-852 and R-842 radios, and an SPU-7 intercom system. A four-channel autopilot is installed that controls the helicopter's roll, yaw, altitude, and course. The autopilot allows the pilot to make inputs or override the autopilot without disengaging the system. The extensive navigation and communications equipment installed on the Mi-8 allows the Hip to operate under all weather conditions and at night.

During the development of the Hip a great deal of attention was given to making the helicopter simple to maintain. Maintenance of the engines, main reduction gear, transmission, and rotor head can be accomplished in the field without special equipment. For ease of maintenance the engine cowlings and access panels are stressed to serve as work platforms for maintenance personnel. Access to the engine compartment and upper fuselage is made through a hatch in the cockpit roof.

This Aeroflot Mi-8P Hip (CCCP-11052) was the first example shown in the West when it was displayed at the 26th Aerosalon at Le Bourget in 1965. American pilots allowed to fly the aircraft were, according to Soviet sources, quite impressed with the Mi-8's handling qualities and flight characteristics.

A Hip C (Mi-8P) of the People's Republic of China Air Force preparing to depart from a rough concrete helopad is one of at least forty Hips in service with the Chinese Air Force. A number of others are in service with the Civil Aviation Administration of China (CAAC). The overall Light Gray Hip has the serial number painted in Red on the tail boom.

Mi-8P

The first Mi-8s off the production line were civil models delivered to Aeroflot as commercial twenty-four passenger helicopters under the designation Mi-8P. Aviaexport, the Soviet Foreign Trade Company for aircraft and helicopter sales, offered a variant of the Mi-8P for commercial export with provision for thirty-two seats. Civil passenger variants are equipped with a baggage compartment, toilet facilities, and airstairs installed in the rear clamshell doors. An executive variant, designated the Mi-8S (Salon), was demonstrated at the Paris Air Show in 1971 and could be configured for nine to eleven passengers in a plush interior with a couch, large seats, tables, and a galley.

Crews flying the Hip in operational service pointed out the need for improvements in cabin heat and lateral control. To correct the heating problem the starboard external strap-on fuel tank was fitted with a cabin heater mounted in the forward half of the tank.

Mi-8T

The success of the Mi-8P led Mil to develop a utility transport variant under the designation Mi-8T. The Mi-8T had the large rectangular cabin windows replaced with

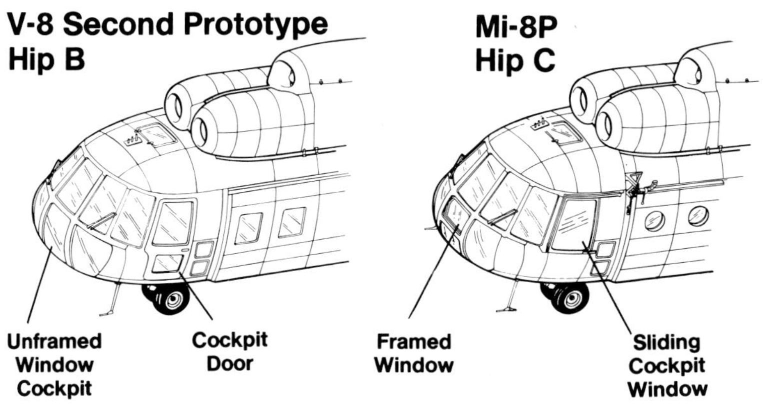

The vast remote areas of the Soviet Union makes the use of helicopters a necessity. A late production Aeroflot Hip C (Mi-8P) delivers its passengers to a remote area during 1983. The hoist over the cabin door was standard on all late production Mi-8Ps. This Hip is White with the nose and fuselage stripe in Blue. The Aeroflot logo and registration are in Black.

smaller round windows (although a number of early production Mi-8Ts were delivered with rectangular windows), the clamshell rear loading doors were enlarged, hook on ramps for loading vehicles and outsized cargo were provided, and a hoist was mounted on the port side of the fuselage above the rear sliding cabin door.

Further improvements on the Mi-8T included replacing the small 'L' shaped RV-3 radio altimeter transceiver antennas with small round dielectric antennas mounted on the underside of the tail boom and a DIW-1 Doppler radar in a box type fairing was mounted under the forward portion of the tail boom. The Doppler radar allows accurate measurements of drift and airspeed while in a hover or during low speed, low altitude maneuvering. The three pole SRO-2M Odd Rods IFF antennas were relocated from the top of the cockpit to below the fuselage in front of the nose wheel.

Both the MI-8P and MI-8T can be easily converted to an ambulance configuration with a capacity for twelve stretchers and seats for medical personnel.

Military transport variants of the Mi-8T are assigned the NATO code name Hip C. The Hip C is the standard Warsaw Pact transport helicopter and is capable of carrying up to twenty-four fully equipped troops. The circular fuselage windows can be locked in an open position while in flight to allow infantrymen on board to use their weapons.

Starboard Strap-on Fuel Tank

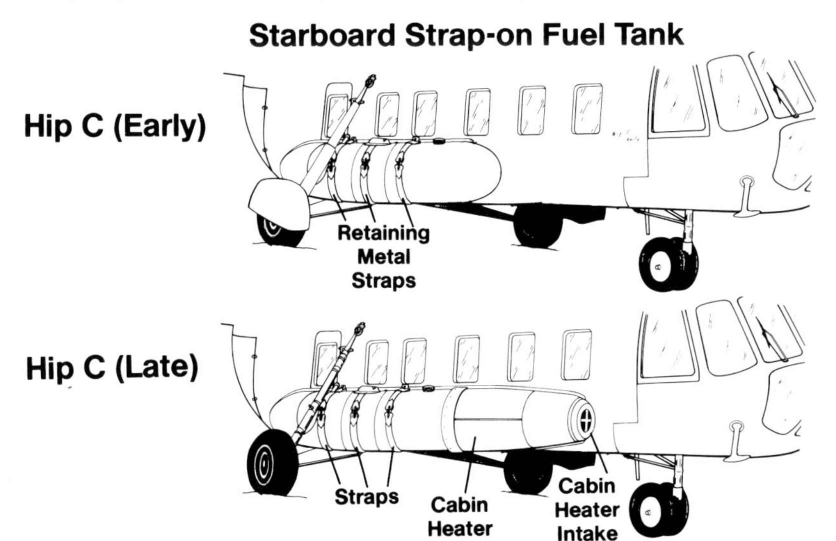

A pair of Hip Cs (Mi-8P) of the *Luftstreitkräfte der Nationalen Volksarmee* (German Democratic Republic Air Force) in early 1979. The intake for the cabin heater, installed in the forward portion of the strap-on fuel tank, is just below the open cockpit window.

Peru is the sole South American country to use the Hip. Three aircraft were donated by the Soviets after an earthquake in 1970 and were followed by thirty Hip Cs in 1978. This Dark Green over Blue Gray Peruvian Army Hip C, based at Collique-Lima airfield during July of 1985, carries the serial number in White on the tail boom and nose. The fuselage roundel is pierced by a sword with a Silver blade and Yellow hilt.

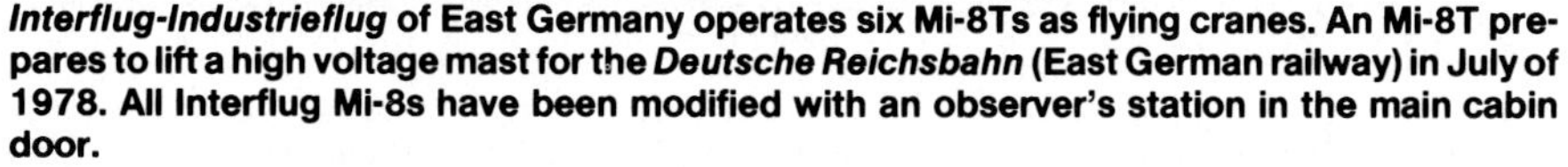

Interflug-Industrieflug of East Germany operates six Mi-8Ts as flying cranes. An Mi-8T prepares to lift a high voltage mast for the *Deutsche Reichsbahn* (East German railway) in July of 1978. All Interflug Mi-8s have been modified with an observer's station in the main cabin door.

Soviet workers unload crates from the spacious main cabin of an Aeroflot Hip C (CCCP 25886) during 1978. The enlarged rear clamshell cargo doors and Doppler radar housing under the tail boom were introduced on the Mi-8T.

Workers at a coal mine in Siberia board an Mi-8T of the Soviet State Airline Aeroflot, the World's largest airline. An ex-military aircraft, this Hip C retains its military Dark Green over Light Gray color scheme with the Aeroflot lettering in Black over the cabin windows. In any conflict Aeroflot Mi-8s would return to military service.

Rear Cargo Doors

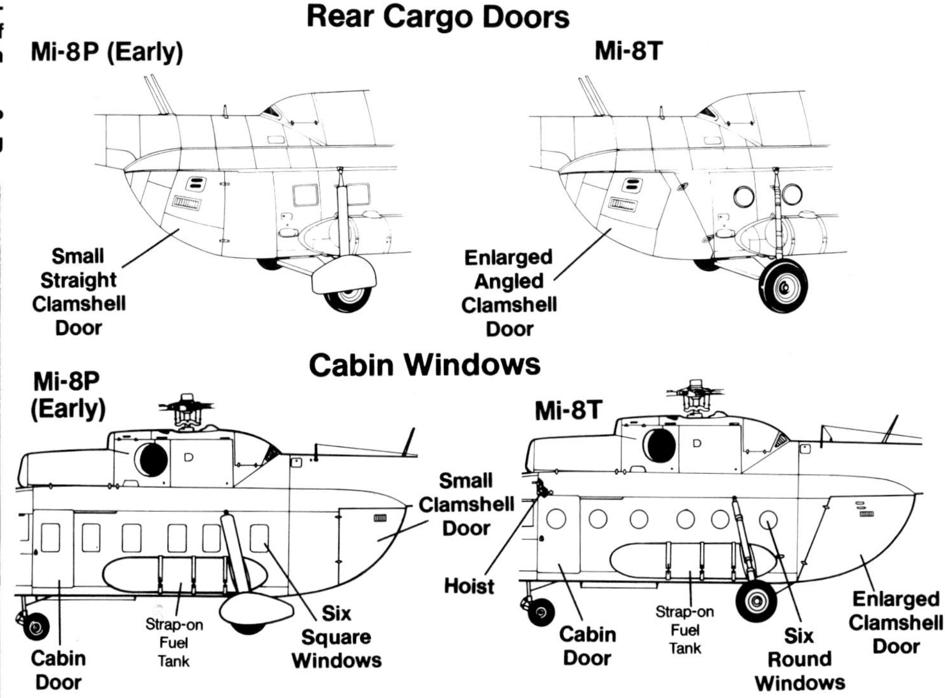

(Above) One of at least three overall White Hip Cs of the *Polska Lotnicza Eskadra Pomocy Etipii* (Polish Relief Helicopter Squadron) on a mercy flight over Ethiopia in March of 1985. The aircraft number (641) and 'Polish Relief Helicopter Squadron in Ethiopia' is in Black with the squadron's insignia carried on the fuselage behind the cockpit sliding window.

(Right) The intake plugs of this Earth Brown and Olive Drab camouflaged Hip C are in Red. There is a First Aid kit mounted on the bulkhead behind the pilot's seat. The rescue hoist is standard equipment on all late production Hips.

(Below Right) A Soviet Hip C (Mi-8T), 'Yellow 01' has its cockpit covered with a tarp and the exhausts sealed with metal covers. The upper surface camouflage is Olive Green while the undersurfaces are Light Blue. The two raked antennas on top of the tail boom are VHF radio antennas.

Doppler Radar Housing

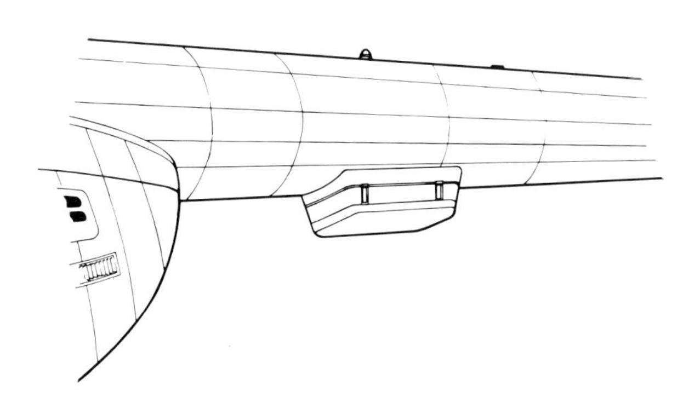

Armed Variants —Hip C, E, and F

During the mid-1960's the Soviets were closely following US and European armed helicopter experiments and the early American use of armed helicopters in Vietnam. These observations led the Mil OKB to develop an armed variant of the Mi-8. A standard weapons configuration was tested and approved for installation on the Mi-8T. It consisted of bolt-on outriggers capable of mounting two weapons pylons on each side of the fuselage. After a series of successful tests, the armed variant of the Mi-8T was put into production under the Soviet designation Mi-8TB. NATO made no distinction between the transport Hip C and the armed Hip C; both were designated Hip C.

Initial armament carried on the armed Mi-8TB was four UB-16 sixteen shot 57 MM rocket pods. Later these were replaced by larger UB-32 rocket pods each holding thirty-two S-5 shaped charge 57MM rockets. The outrigger pylons can also accommodate bombs up to 550 pounds, gun pods or chemical spray tanks.

Hip E

Further experiments with helicopter armament led to a more heavily armed variant of the Mi-8, the Mi-8TBK, NATO code name Hip E. The Hip E carried an additional pylon on each fuselage outrigger, four rails for anti-tank missiles mounted above the outrigger pylons, and an Afanasyev 12.7 MM machine gun in the nose. In combat the gun is fired by the flight engineer/gunner sitting between the two pilots. A gyro-stabilized missile control/gunsight is installed over the starboard seat and is operated by the co-pilot. A fully loaded Mi-8TBK carries a total of 192 unguided S-5 rockets (six 32 shot pods) and four AT-2 radio command guided, line of sight anti-tank missiles (NATO code name Swatter) plus the internal gun.

Hip F

An export variant of the Mi-8TBK was later identified in East Germany and this helicopter received the NATO code name Hip F. It is believed that the German Democratic Republic Air Force is the sole user of this variant. Instead of four AT-2 missiles, the Hip F mounts six AT-3 wire guided anti-tank missiles (NATO code name Sagger) making it the world's most heavily armed gunship helicopter. It is believed that the East Germans modified a number of Mi-8TBKs to the Hip F configuration before the Soviet Union released the improved Swatter (AT-2) missile for export. A fully armed and fueled Mi-8TBK is reportedly very heavy and unresponsive, with little power reserve for maneuverability, especially at low altitudes. Because of the extra weight of the weapons only twelve troops can be carried.

A number of Mi-8 variants have been developed for specialized missions and are known under their NATO code names, including the:

Hip D airborne communications variant with large antennas mounted on the upper and lower tail boom and along the fuselage sides. The Hip D is used for both air-to-air and air-to-ground communications relay.

Hip G airborne Communications variant with an antenna projecting rearward from the rear of the cabin and additional antennas and a doppler radar mounted on the tail boom.

Hip J electronic counter measures (ECM) variant identified by two small boxes mounted on both sides of the fuselage ahead and behind the main landing gear strut.

Hip K communications jamming electronic warfare variant with a large multiple antenna array on each side of the rear fuselage.

The Mi-8 has become the most widely used helicopter in the Warsaw Pact and figures

A Tan and Medium Green over Light Blue camouflaged Hungarian Air Force Hip C gunship (Mi-8TB) takes off with a load of skydivers during an airshow. at Buda-Örs in the Summer of 1987. The serial number 10427 on the tail boom is in Red with a thin White outline. The fire truck on the left is an East German built Type W-50 fire/rescue truck built by I.F.A.

An early production Czechoslovakian Air Force Hip C (Mi-8TB) gunship, 'White 0910' has the rotor blades tied down to prevent wind damage while on the ground. The fuselage outrigger pylons are non-standard and were later improved with additional support struts. The IFF antenna on top of the cockpit is covered to protect it during servicing.

Soviet airborne troops deploy from a pair of Hip C gunships (Mi-8TB). The Hip C can carry twenty-eight fully equipped troops or a jeep sized vehicle. A Soviet Assault Helicopter Regiment usually includes a Hip squadron and two Hind squadrons.

The Polish Air Force operates several variants of the Hip. 'White 612' in the foreground is a Hip C gunship (Mi-8TB), while 'White 720' in the background is one of the few Hip C transports (Mi-8P) in Polish service. The open hatch on top of the cockpit is the access hatch to the upper fuselage.

prominently in Soviet/WARPAC tactical exercises and war planning. Some 1,615 Mi-8s are currently in front line service with the helicopter regiments of Soviet Frontal Aviation. The Hip has seen combat in the Middle East, Africa, Asia, and Central America.

Egyptian commandos used a number of Hip Cs and Es in their assault across the Suez Canal during the 1973 Yom Kippur War. Soviet commanders in Ethiopia used the Mi-8 to ferry Cuban and Ethiopian troops behind Somalian lines during the Ethiopia/Somalia Ogaden border war. Vietnamese Hips have seen action in Cambodia, while Sandinista Hip Es have been used against Contra Freedom Fighters in Nicaragua. Reports from Afghanistan tell of both Soviet and Afghanistani flown Mi-8s being used both for close air support and chemical warfare during the fighting in that war torn country.

The Mi-8, however, has also been used for more peaceful missions. Three Mi-8s were donated to the Peruvian government following a disastrous earthquake in 1970. The Polish Relief Helicopter Squadron in Ethiopia used three MI-8Ts to fly famine-relief operations during 1985, often working in close cooperation with Western agencies such as the Royal Air Force C-130 Hercules detachment.

A pair of Hip Fs (Mi-8TBK) of the East German Air Force on an exercise in southern East Germany in September of 1980 carry six silver UB-32 rocket pods, however, the missile rails for the Sagger (AT-3) anti-tank missiles are empty. A 12.7MM machine gun is mounted in the nose and fired by the flight engineer.

An armed Hip C gunship (Mi-8TB) of the *Hubschraubergeschwader Werner Seelenbinder* of the East German Air Force lowers a sling load of cargo during an exercise in October of 1985. The Mi-8 is capable of carrying 6,000 pounds of underslung cargo. The UB-16 rocket pods and aircraft number (7400) on the tail boom are Black.

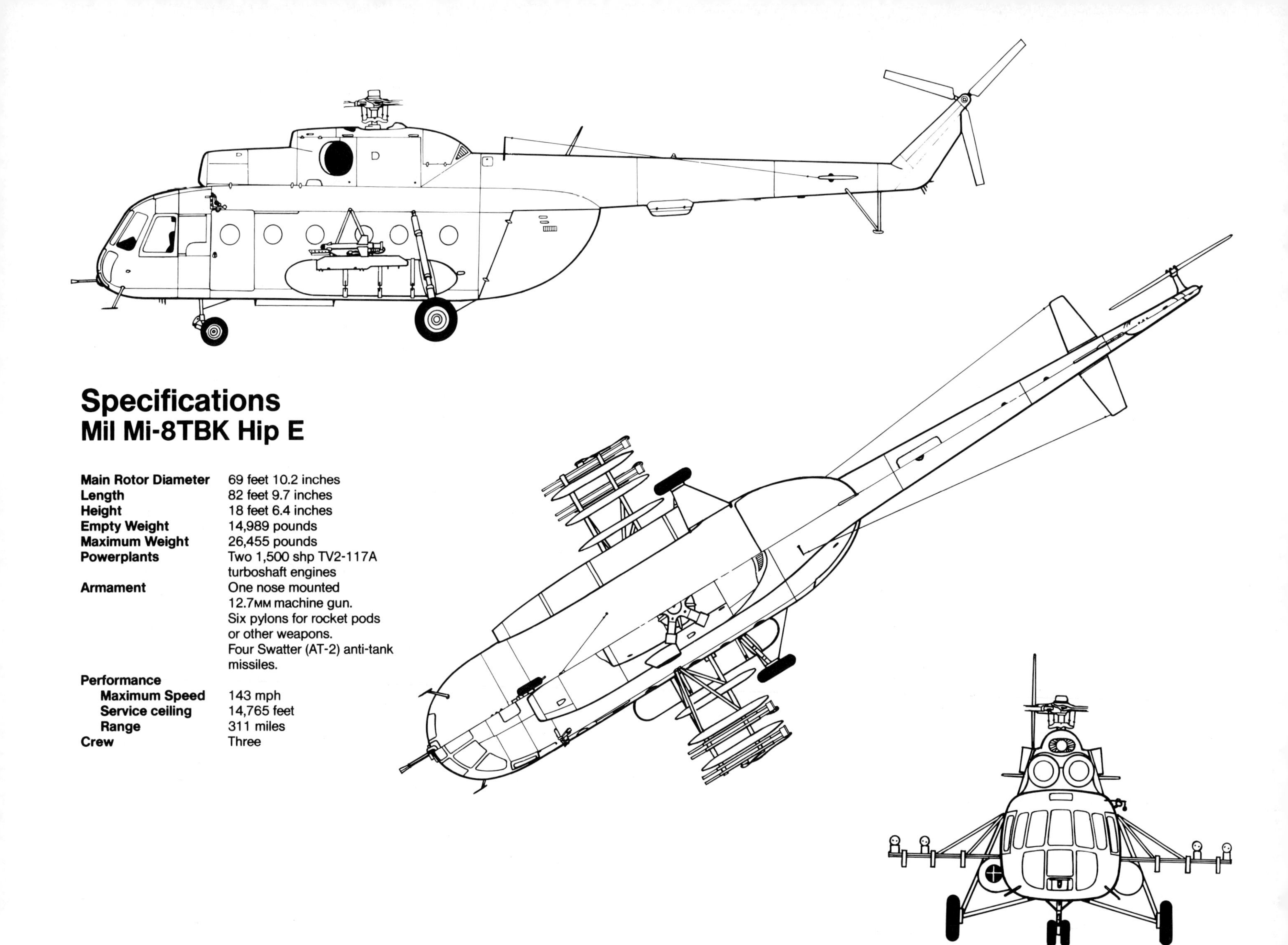

Specifications
Mil Mi-8TBK Hip E

Main Rotor Diameter	69 feet 10.2 inches
Length	82 feet 9.7 inches
Height	18 feet 6.4 inches
Empty Weight	14,989 pounds
Maximum Weight	26,455 pounds
Powerplants	Two 1,500 shp TV2-117A turboshaft engines
Armament	One nose mounted 12.7MM machine gun. Six pylons for rocket pods or other weapons. Four Swatter (AT-2) anti-tank missiles.
Performance	
Maximum Speed	143 mph
Service ceiling	14,765 feet
Range	311 miles
Crew	Three

A flight of East German Air Force Hip Fs enroute to a landing zone during Exercise Brotherhood in Arms '80 held in September of 1980. The Hip Fs carry silver UB-32 pods, but no AT-3 Swatter missiles. There are at least seventy-five Hip Fs in service with the *Luftstreitkräfte*.

The Hip F (Mi-8TBK) is the most heavily armed combat helicopter in the world. Fully loaded with six rocket pods, six missiles and a nose mounted machine gun, the Hip F is reportedly unmaneuverable and has demanding flight characteristics. The different shapes of the port and starboard external fuel tanks are due to the installation of a cabin heater in the front of the starboard tank.

Hip Fs of the East German Navy are frequently employed in Search and Rescue operations. The crew of this *Volksmarine* Hip F practice SAR techniques during a training exercise in May of 1982. The Black tactical number 808 identifies this Hip as belonging to a training unit.

Over 8,000 Mi-8s were built before production was phased out in favor of a more powerful variant, the Mi-17 Hip H. A large number of Mi-8s have been exported both commercially and militarily and serve in some forty-two countries including:

Afghanistan	Algeria	Angola	Bangladesh
Bulgaria	China	Cuba	Czechoslovakia
Egypt	Ethiopia	Finland	East Germany
Guinea-Bissau	Guyana	Hungary	India
Iraq	Japan	Kampuchea (Cambodia)	Laos
Libya	Madagascar	Mali	Mongolia
Mozambique	Nicaragua	North Korea	Pakistan
Peru	Poland	Romania	Somalia
Sudan	Syria	Uganda	USA
Vietnam	Yemen	South Yemen	Yugoslavia
Zambia			

Additionally, the Hip was evaluated by British European Airways, although no order was placed and a number of captured ex-Egyptian Hips are believed to be in service with the Israeli Defense Force Air Force for second line duties.

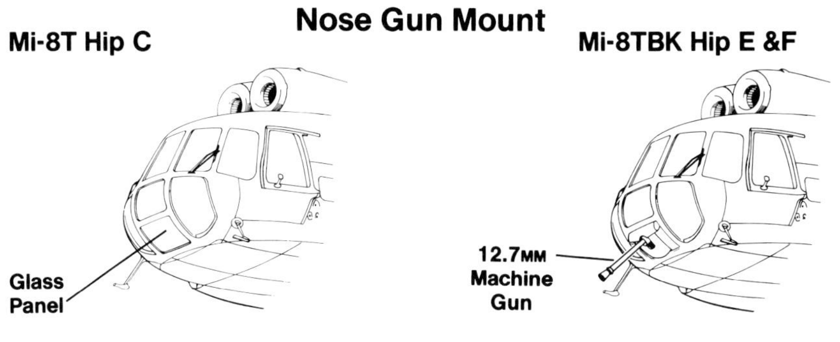

The crew of an Mi-8 includes the pilot, co-pilot, and in some cases a flight engineer as carried on this mission during the Winter of 1980. The pilot normally flys the aircraft while the co-pilot is responsible for navigation.

A Sandinista (Nicaraguan) Air Force Mi-8TB in a jungle clearing has deployed troops for another search mission against Contra Freedom Fighters. The Mi-8s arrived in Nicaragua as deck cargo aboard Soviet freighters and have seen extensive service in the Nicaraguan civil war.

A maintenance technician checks out the engine on a Hip C using the stressed engine and transmission access panels as maintenance platforms. The Mi-8 was designed to be serviced in the field without the need of special tools or work stands.

Outrigger Pylons

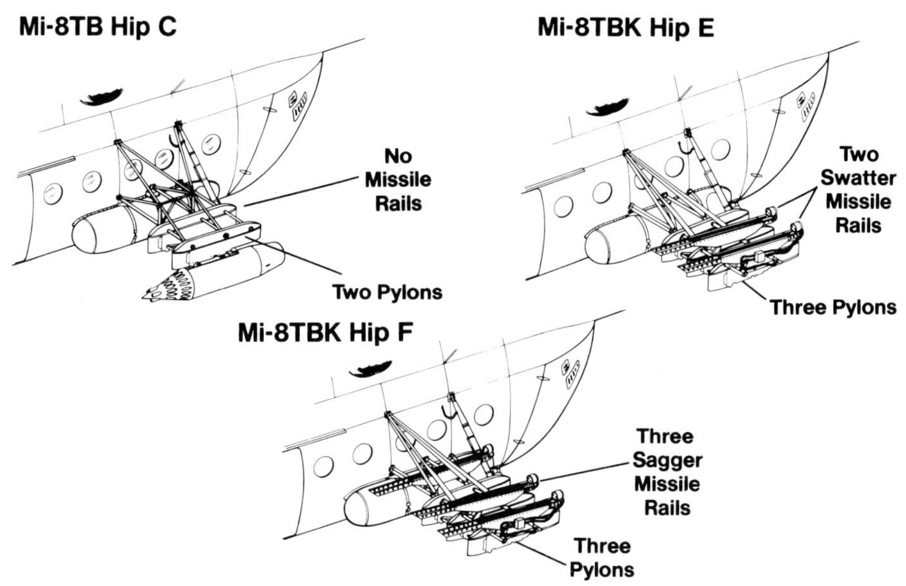

V-24 Prototype

Published reports of American helicopter combat operations in Vietnam were widely circulated and studied in the Soviet Union. These reports showed that the standard armed troop carrier helicopter, the Bell UH-1 Huey, was too slow, overweight, unresponsive, and too lightly armed to be an effective gunship. These reports also revealed that loss rates for helicopters in combat were much lower than had been expected.

During the Vietnam War the United States lost 2,281 helicopters in combat, however, when compared with the total number of combat hours flown during Vietnam the loss rate averaged one aircraft for every 6,629 hours. This low loss rate was attributed to the US Army's tactics of supporting troop carrier helicopters with gunships, such as the UH-1D Huey gunship and Bell AH-1 Huey Cobra. The gunship proved to be an effective platform for ground support, destroying enemy tanks, as well as convoy escort.

The American study highly influenced Soviet helicopter development and the value of a heavily armed assault helicopter gained favor in Soviet military circles. To Soviet generals the idea of a rotary winged *Stromovick* was highly appealing. In World War II, the heavily armed and armored Ilyushin Il-2 *Stromovick* was highly effective against German armor. A heavily armed and armored helicopter would be of similar value on the modern battlefield, providing ground forces with a mobile platform capable of ground support against enemy troops and armored vehicles unconstrained by terrain or tactical obstructions such as mine fields.

Soviet military doctrine, however, required a helicopter with both a heavy weapons load *and the capability of carrying troops*. This contrasts sharply with Western design philosophy where troops are not carried by gunships. As a result American, French, and British gunships are smaller, faster, and more maneuverable than their counterparts behind the Iron Curtain.

In 1966 the Soviet Government issued a requirement for a dedicated helicopter gunship to the Mil OKB. Progress on the new gunship design was initially hampered because Mil was heavily engaged in the development of the Mil V-12 Homer, in the event the Homer project was canceled freeing the Mil OKB to concentrate on the gunship project.

The Mil OKB approached the gunship program in a typically Russian manner, using modified components of proven designs. Although derived from the Mi-8, the gunship would be smaller and more powerful. The fuselage was a conventional all metal, semi-monocoque pod and boom structure with retractable landing gear. Two stub wings (similar to those of the Mi-6) were included for weapons pylons and to add lift at high speeds. With a crew of three and eight troops the design had a projected top speed of over 186 mph.

Because Mikhail Mil was terminally ill with cancer (he died on 31 January 1970) the project was placed under the leadership of Marat Tishchenko. The first prototype was completed during 1969 under the designation V-24 and began a series of factory tests. The prototype was powered by two 1,700 shp TV2-117A engines mounted side by side above the main cabin. The crew of three, pilot, navigator, and engineer/gunner were housed under a long greenhouse canopy. Eight troops could be carried in the central cabin which was equipped with large exit doors on each side of the fuselage. The doors were divided horizontally with the upper half opening upward and the lower portion opening downward with a boarding step built in to the lower door half. Four small rectangular windows were installed on either side of the main cabin. These windows, like those on the MI-8, could be opened in flight and were equipped with gunmounts for AK-47 assault rifles.

The tail boom was faired into the fuselage aft of the cabin and fitted with all moving horizontal stabilizers. The vertical stabilizer housed the tail rotor gear box and drive shaft with the rotor mounted on the starboard side. The five bladed main rotor was of similar configuration to the Mi-8 but smaller in diameter and turned at higher rpms. The oil cooler, rotor mast and auxiliary power unit (APU) were mounted above the engines in a faired housing that gave the appearance of a third engine. The intake for the APU is installed immediately behind the rotor mast with the exhaust on the port side of the fairing.

A pre-production V-24 on a test flight during 1971. The V-24 had straight stub wings and four weapons pylons. Western intelligence agencies did not discover the existence of the V-24 until after production Hinds had entered service. The aircraft were given the NATO code name Hind B even though they were actually earlier variants.

The strait shoulder mounted stub wings were located above and behind the main cabin. The stub wings provided a twenty-five percent increase in lift during high speed flight, reduced turning radius, and additional space for a pair of weapons pylons on each wing. The wings, however, did cause some loss of performance in a hover by interfering with the rotor downwash. The prototype was fitted with a fully retractable tricycle landing gear. The steerable nose wheel was mounted under the forward fuselage retracting into a bay under the cockpit. The main landing gear rotated ninety degrees, retracting into bays on the fuselage below and behind the main cabin.

During 1971 the first prototype was joined by two pre-production aircraft and these aircraft were used to conduct a series of operational tests. During the test program one aircraft was fitted with a 'fenestron' shrouded tail rotor system, similar to that developed for the Aerospatiale SA 330 Gazelle. The tests proved unsuccessful and the 'fenestron' project was cancelled. Because their existence was not discovered until after appearance of the first production aircraft (Hind A), the prototype and pre-production gunships were given the NATO name Hind B.

After completion of factory and State Acceptance trials the V-24 was approved for production under the designation Mi-24. Production of the gunship was assigned to the State Aircraft Factories at Arsenyev and Rostov with the first production aircraft being delivered to the Soviet Air Force during 1972.

Mi-24 Hind A

Production Hind As differed from the prototype and pre-production aircraft in a number of ways. The stub wings were completely redesigned with a pronounced anhedral and a flat end plate on the outer wing panel. The end plate also served as a pylon that mounted two missile rails for AT-2 Swatter anti-tank missiles.

This standard Soviet anti-tank weapon (also used on both ground and vehicle mounts) was selected to be the missile armament for the Mi-24. The Swatter is a radio command guided cylindrical missile weighing sixty pounds with a length of 3 feet 9.75 inches. The missile has four small forward control fins and four larger wing fins spaning 2 feet 2 inches mounted on the rear body of the missile. The Swatter has a speed of 335 mph and can hit targets at ranges from 1,640 to 11,500 feet.

To provide guidance for the missiles, an AT-2 missile director pod was mounted under the nose of the Hind A. Other changes to the Hind A included: deletion of the antenna mounted on the top of the vertical stabilizer, installation of a gun camera on the inboard port pylon, redesigned Doppler radar cover, addition of crew boarding steps below the cockpit on the port side, and a short wave aerial was installed under the rear portion of the fuselage.

Extensive communications and navigational electronics are carried on the Hind A. Standard all weather navigational equipment includes: an ARL radio compass, RV-5 radio altimeter, MPR-56P radio beacon receiver, Type SP 50 ILS transceiver, GIK-1 gyro compass, and an RSBN-25 short range navigation system. Communications equipment is equally extensive and includes a Landysk 5 VHF radio, Type Mikron UHF radio, and a Type SPU-7 intercom.

Yellow 36 of the 16th Air Army, Group of Soviet Forces in Germany (GSFG). Hind As were first observed by the West when they deployed to East Germany in 1973. Within a year two Hind A regiments were based at the former *Luftwaffe* bases of Stendal and Parchim. Early Hind As carried the Odd Rods IFF antenna on the center cockpit canopy frame.

Early Hind As had the tail rotor on the starboard side of the vertical stabilizer. The tail rotor is Black with Red-White-Red warning stripes on the blade tips. Forward view for the pilot is restricted by the gunner and his sighting equipment.

The cockpit floor and crew seats were protected with steel armor plate, however, the canopy was plexiglas rather than armor glass. Fuel tanks were self sealing and filled with an inert gas to prevent fire from crash or battle damage. An external cargo hook could be installed on the fuselage underside allowing the Mi-24 to lift external loads up to 6,000 pounds.

Normal armament carried on the Hind A consisted of four UB-32 thirty-two shot rocket pods, or FAB 250 550 pound high explosive bombs, four Swatter (AT-2) ,missiles on the stub wing racks, and a single Afanasyev A 12.7MM machine gun on a flexible mount in the center nose section. The gun is operated by the gunner/observer and although on a flexible mount the angle of fire is, however, somewhat limited. Other armament options include UB-16 rocket pods, fuel tanks, and gun pods.

During the Spring of 1973 the first Hind As were deployed to the German Democratic Republic (DDR) as part of the Group of Soviet Forces in Germany (GSFG). By the Spring of 1974 two regiments of forty-five aircraft each were assigned to the 16th Air Army, which is responsible for the capture of Berlin in the event of war. Hind As were based at the GSFG airfields of Parchim and Stendal, both west of Berlin.

The appearance of Hind As in East Germany came as quite a shock for NATO which, at the time, had no helicopter of equal performance and firepower to counter the Mi-24. NATO armor crews reportedly gave the Hind A another name, one that reflected their

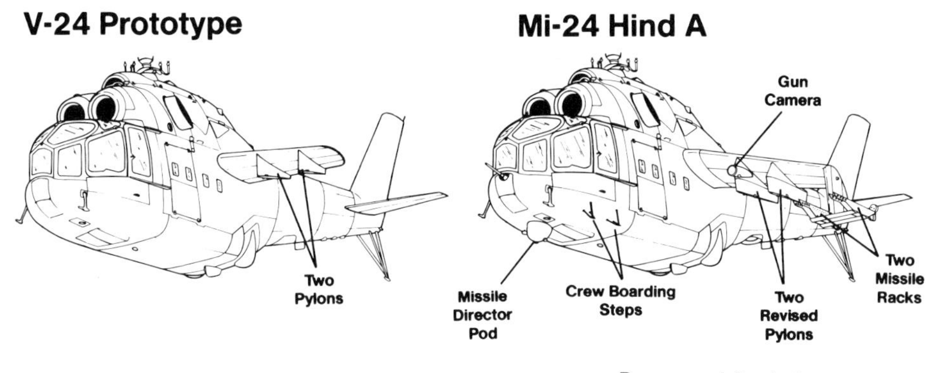

White 02, an early Hind A powered by 1,700 hp Izotov TV-117-A engines carries four UB-32 rocket pods on the stub wing pylons. The bulge under the nose is the Swatter missile guidance pod. The Hind A could carry eight fully equipped troops in the center cabin.

A Hind A of the Soviet Occupation Forces in Afghanistan. The Hind A is used by both the Soviet Air Force and regular Afghan Air Force, however, most were withdrawn from combat after a relatively short period of operations.

impressions of the gunship's impressive firepower, speed, size, and fearsome appearance. NATO tank crews called the Mi-24 the *Bogeyman* — their worst nightmares come true.

The Hind A is not a total *Bogeyman* however — it has its shortcomings. Its large size provides the helicopter a number of built-in tactical disadvantages. Its deep fuselage gives the Hind a high radar signature making it easy to detect and track with radar guided anti-aircraft weapons. Its overall size causes a loss of maneuverability at low speeds and also makes it is easy to see and track visually. With a length of some fifty-five feet the Mi-24A is roughly the same size as a World War II medium bomber.

Hind A (late)

Early production Hind As were powered by the reliable 1,700 shp Izotov TV-2-117A engine. When the more powerful 2,200 shp Izotov TV-3-117 turboshaft engine became available, the engine compartment of the Hind A was redesigned to accept the more powerful engine. The TV-3-117 was also selected to power an advanced variant of the Mi-8 Hip under the designation Mi-17, NATO code name Hip H. The use of the same engine in both the Mi-24 and Mi-17 simplified production and gave Soviet commanders the advantage of being able to use the same spare engine parts for either helicopter.

Besides the engine change the modified Hind A had the tail rotor relocated to the port side of the vertical fin and geared to rotate in the opposite direction. The change from a 'pusher' to a 'puller' configuration improved the helicopter's control responses, particularly in yaw control and eliminated the aerodynamic masking from the vertical stabilizer that had been a problem with the earlier tail rotor system.

Additionally the modified Hind A had the Odd Rods IFF antenna repositioned from the center cockpit frame to the top of the oil cooler intake and also deleted the short wave antenna that had been mounted under the fuselage.

Later in the production run Hind As were modified with the addition of seven external fuselage re-enforcing ribs installed on the port side of the fuselage behind the wing and a modified horizontal stabilizer.

A Hind A provides top cover for a Soviet Army T-62 tank on a powered ferry pontoon during a river crossing exercise. Close co-operation between ground troops and helicopters is practiced during every Warsaw Pact field exercise.

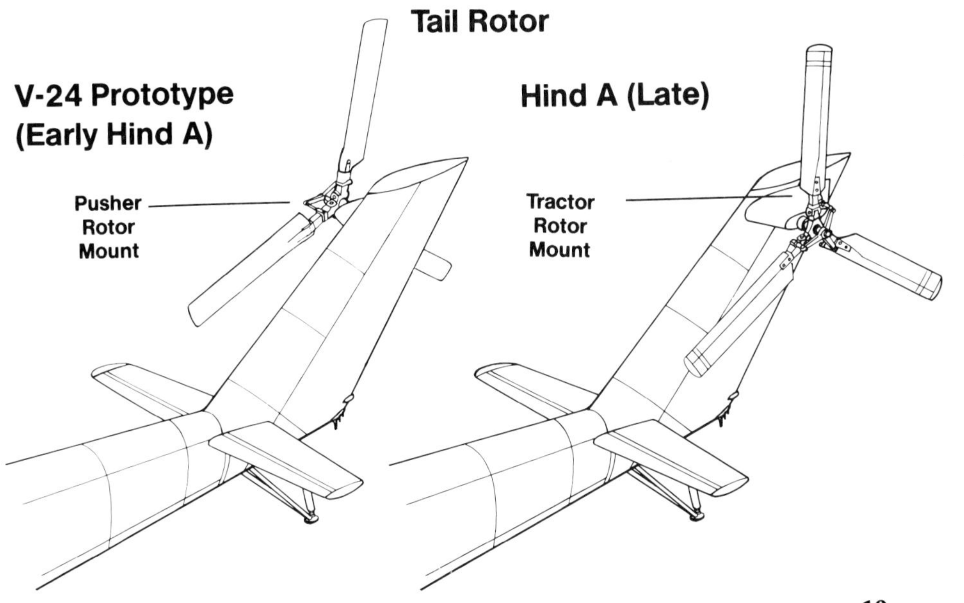

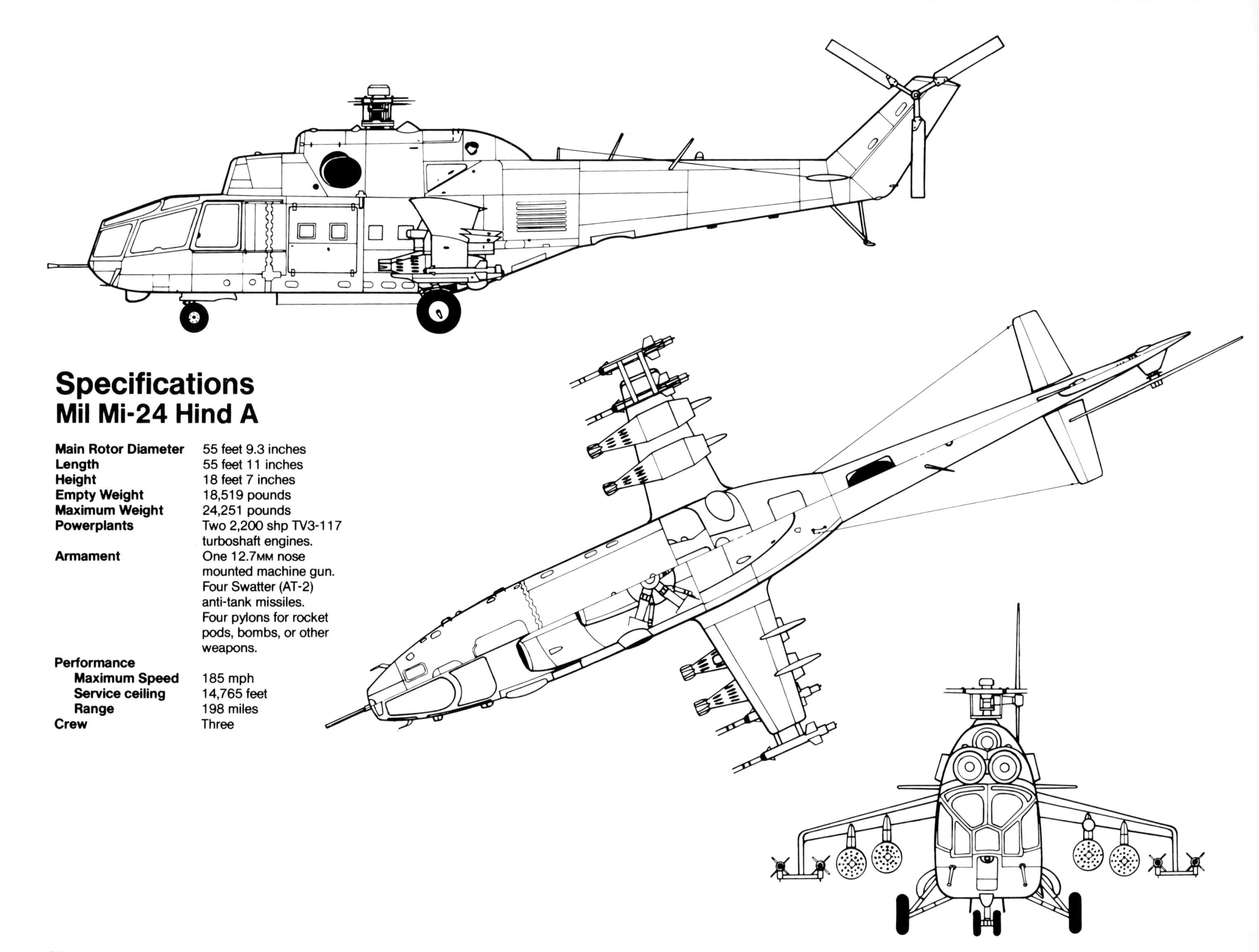

Specifications
Mil Mi-24 Hind A

Main Rotor Diameter	55 feet 9.3 inches
Length	55 feet 11 inches
Height	18 feet 7 inches
Empty Weight	18,519 pounds
Maximum Weight	24,251 pounds
Powerplants	Two 2,200 shp TV3-117 turboshaft engines.
Armament	One 12.7MM nose mounted machine gun. Four Swatter (AT-2) anti-tank missiles. Four pylons for rocket pods, bombs, or other weapons.
Performance	
Maximum Speed	185 mph
Service ceiling	14,765 feet
Range	198 miles
Crew	Three

The landing gear on the Hind A is fully retractable. The nosewheel retracted rearward into a bay under the cockpit while the main gear retracts into wells on the fuselage sides behind the main cabin. The 'L' shaped pitot tubes are carried on both sides of the nose.

The Hind A was exported to three Soviet client states: Algeria, Afghanistan and Libya. Production of the Hind A was phased out during 1975 after some 550 aircraft were built. The Hind A has been withdrawn from Soviet front line combat regiments, however, a number of aircraft remain in service outside the Soviet Union. A dedicated training version was built in small numbers and received the NATO code name Hind C. The Hind C had the nose gun, missile guidance pack, and missile rails deleted, but was otherwise externally identical to the Hind A.

A-10 Record Aircraft

During 1975 a modified version of the Mi-24 Hind A under the designation A-10, captured eight World Records for helicopter performance and set eleven Soviet National Records. The A-10 was powered by 2,200 shp Izotov TV-2-117A engines and had all armor, armament, and unnecessary equipment removed to save weight. The stub wings, however, were retained since they supported the rotor at high speeds.

These record flights were flown by a female crew. The pilot was Galina Rastorgueva (daughter of the famous Soviet test pilot Victor Rastorgueva) and the navigator was Ludmila Polyanskaya. Both crew members belonged to the civilian Soviet *Valerj Tshkalov* Aeroclub.

The series of record capturing flights began on 16 July 1975. The first record was for speed over a closed course. The A-10 established a new Class E (Helicopter) record when it reached a speed of 212.09 mph over the 15/25 kilometer (9.32/15.54 mile) course. Two days later another record was set for speed over a 100 kilometer closed course (207.82 mph). On 8 August a new helicopter time to climb record was set (9,843 feet in 2 minutes 33.5 seconds). On 13 August the A-10 captured another speed/distance record with a flight of 621.40 miles at an average speed of 206.69 mph. The last Record flight was on 26 August. The A-10 set a new altitude record of 19,685 feet (in 7 minutes 43 seconds).

The drooped wing and end plates with Swatter missile pylons can be seen well from below on this early production Hind A. The rear sliding bulged side window provided the pilot with a degree of downward vision. A gun camera is carried on the upper port inboard pylon.

Doppler Radar Housing

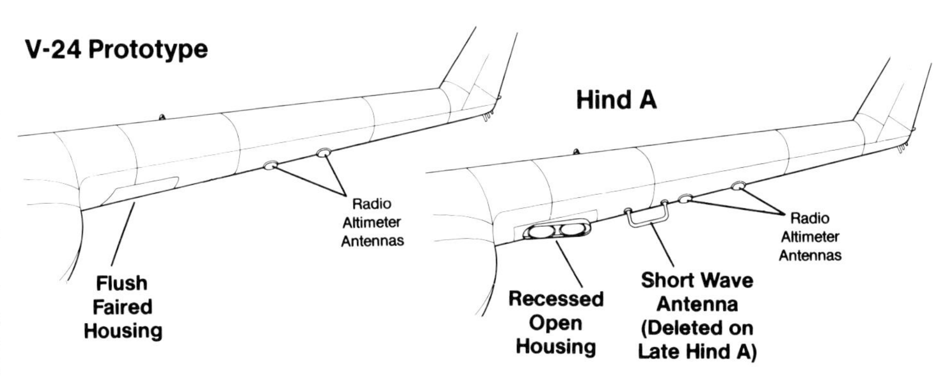

The Hind A can carry a variety of weapons on the stub wing pylons. This Hind A carries a mixed load of two UB-32 rocket pods on the inboard pylons and two FAB 250 500 pound high explosive bombs on the outboard pylons.

The Hind A was first sent to Afghanistan in April of 1979, barely eight months before the Soviets *'came to the assistance of the Afghanistan Government'*, as the Soviet invasion of Afghanistan is reported in the Eastern press.

The crew of a Hind A, pilot, engineer and gunner, head for debriefing after a training mission. Entry to the cockpit is made through the upward opening cockpit side window and rear sliding pilots window on the port side. The 12.7MM machine gun has a limited arc of fire to the side.

Odd Rods IFF Antenna Locations

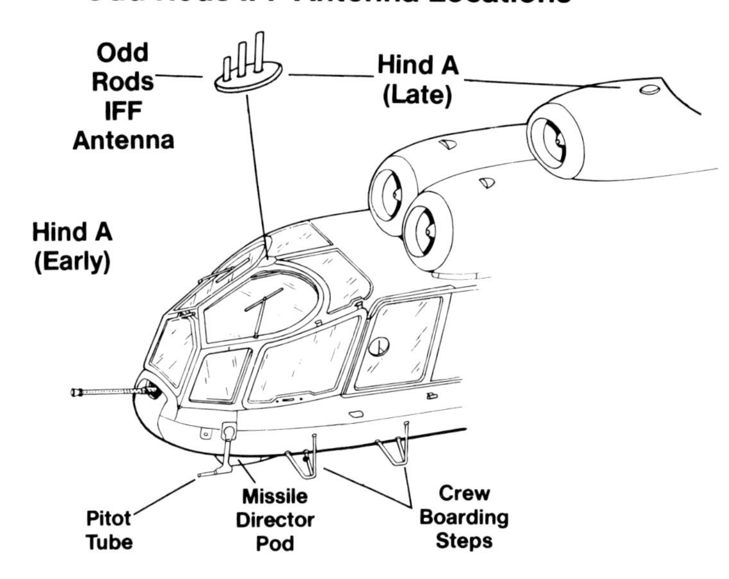

A pair of Soviet Air Force Hind As fly in trail formation low over a swollen river. The lead gunship, Yellow 28, is a standard Hind A, while his wingman, Yellow 23, is a late production variant with the seven external stiffening ribs on the port fuselage side.

The late production Hind A was powered by a pair of 2,200 hp TV-3-117 engines. The tail rotor was moved to the port side of the vertical stabilizer to become a 'tractor' rather than a 'pusher' rotor. A similar engine/tail rotor change was made to the Hip under the designation Mi-17 Hip H.

This late production Hind A is displayed as part of the Soviet Air Force Museum at Monino near Moscow. The seven stiffening ribs added to the late production Hind A can be seen behind the White outlined Red star insignia.

External Rib

Hind A (Early)

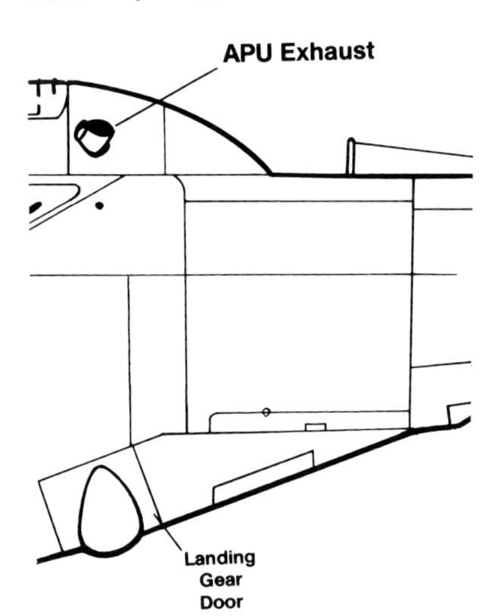

Hind A (Late)

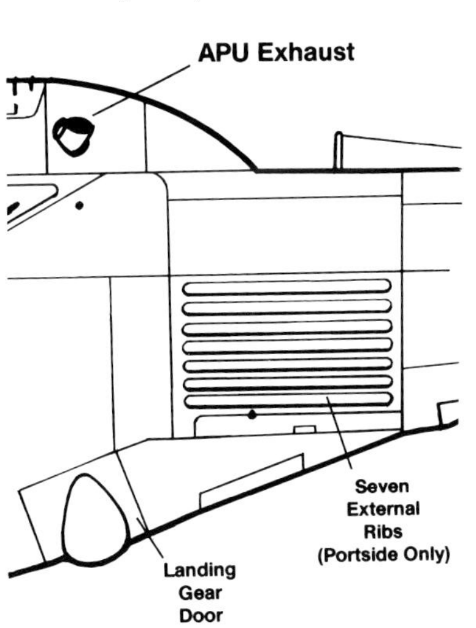

Mi-24 Hind D

Service use of the Hind A by *Frontovaya Aviatsiya* (Frontal Aviation) helicopter regiments quickly showed up a number of needed improvements. Crews complained that the greenhouse cockpit canopy was vulnerable to enemy ground fire, armor protection for both the crew and vital aircraft systems was inadequate, forward vision for the pilot was restricted, and the angle as well as the rate of fire of the 12.7MM machine gun was insufficient. Maintenance personnel reported that rotor blade fatigue life was low and the blades needed to be stronger. These complaints led to a radical redesign of the Hind A.

Mil OKB began work on correcting the Hind A's shortcomings during 1974. Throughout this period the North Vietnamese were providing the Soviets with components from shot down American helicopters. In East Germany a complete rotor system from a Boeing Vertol CH-47 Chinook was put on display as part of an American Vietnam War Equipment exhibit at the Army Museum of the German Democratic Republic in Dresden. Components from the Bell AH-1 Huey Cobra are known to have been evaluated by Soviet engineers. Although it is doubtful that this evaluation had a strong influence on the redesign of the Hind, knowledge of American helicopter technology aided the Soviets greatly in the areas of rotor design, armor, and armament.

Work on the re-designed Hind A was completed in 1975 and when the helicopter first appeared in East Germany during 1976, western observers were surprised by the radical change in appearance of the nose section. NATO assigned the code name Hind D to the variant, even though there was a great deal of argument that this variant should have an entirely new name because the Hind D had the appearance of being a completely new helicopter rather than a re-design of the earlier Hind A.

Although retaining the rotor head, transmission, and basic airframe of the Hind A, the new variant's nose section was completely changed with the pilot and gunner housed in a stepped tandem cockpit with separate canopies for each crewman. The weapons systems operator (WSO) occupied the front cockpit under a hinged starboard opening canopy while the pilot flew the helicopter from a raised rear cockpit with a large rear hinged automobile style door on the starboard side. Each cockpit canopy is equipped with armored glass and the windshields have individual wiper blades.

The front cockpit of the Hind D is equipped with a second set of flight controls for the weapons systems operator, however, the WSO is usually not a fully trained pilot and their skill in flying the aircraft is limited. A station for a flight engineer is provided in the main cabin, although the engineer is not always carried on operations. The entire nose section is heavily armored with armored seats, anti-fragmentation cockpit lining, and armor glass windshields and canopies. The cockpit of the Hind D provides both the WSO and pilot with excellent all-round visibility.

The redesigned nose incorporates a variety of sensors and weapons aiming equipment mounted in external chin pods. A pod with forward-looking Infrared-Red (FLIR) sensors and low light television (LLTV) equipment is installed on the starboard side. FLIR and LLTV allow the Mi-24 to operate at night and under all weather conditions. The sensor pack on the port side of the nose houses the radar director unit for the Swatter (AT-2) missile system. A long air data sensor probe is fitted to the starboard side of the WSO's canopy frame and incorporates sensors for precision input of air data to the

The nose wheel of the Hind D has a longer strut than the Hind A to allow sufficient ground clearance for the nose mounted sensor pods. While the Hind A's nose wheel was fully retractable and covered by doors, the Hind D's nose wheel is semi-retractable and is partially exposed when retracted.

Three early Hind Ds at a helicopter field in East Germany during 1976. The open doors on the two nearest aircraft are pilot entry doors. The gunner's canopy is hinged on the starboard side and opens upwards. The three Hind's are painted in identical camouflage patterns of Light Brown, Medium Brown over Light Blue undersurfaces.

COCKPIT Evolution

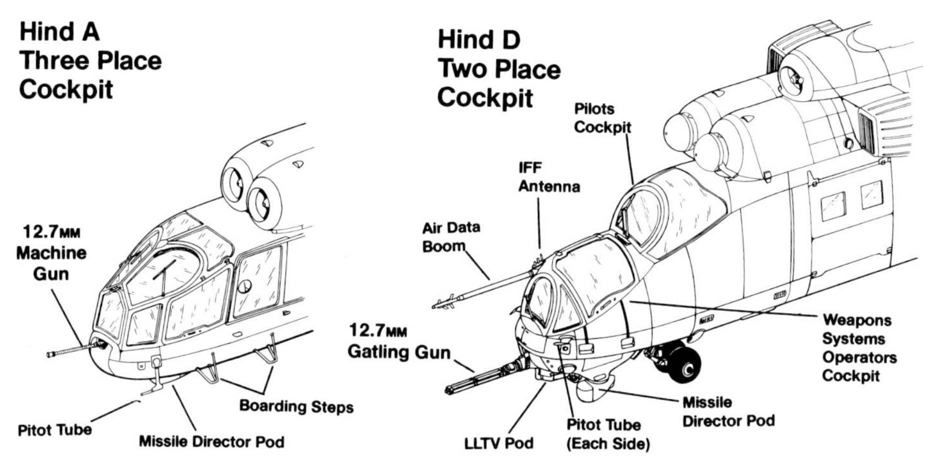

A deadly duo, a Hip F (Mi-8TBK) and Hind D (Mi-24) of the *Adolf von Lützow* Regiment, East German Air Force shortly after take off from an East German base in August of 1981. Warsaw Pact helicopter regiments usually are equipped with both the Hip and Hind.

weapons control and aiming computer. The boom also has an Odd Rods IFF antenna mounted on the attachment fairing just in front of the canopy frame. The fully retractable nose wheel of the Hind A was replaced with a semi-retractable nose wheel with a longer nose wheel strut that increased ground clearance for the nose mounted sensors.

The single 12.7MM machine gun of the Hind A was replaced by a four barrel 12.7MM rotary machine gun capable of firing 800 rounds per minute. The gun is mounted in a turret which can be traversed sixty degrees to either side of the helicopter's centerline. The gun can also be depressed twenty-five degrees and elevated fifteen degrees. The turret gun greatly increases the effectiveness of the helicopter to engage targets without having to maneuver. Ammunition for the gun is limited to 500 rounds. External armament remained the same as that carried on the Hind A.

The Hind D incorporates a number of improvements in communications and navigational radios and radars. A pair of Doppler radar antennas are mounted in a semi-recessed housing under the tail boom, just behind the fuselage fairing. Angled VHF and UHF blade antennas are mounted on top of the tail boom, along with an HF radio antenna with cables running to each stabilizer tip. A short wave communications antenna is mounted under the tail boom behind the Doppler radar housing, followed by two round radio altimeter antennas, and a second Odd Rods IFF antenna array is mounted on the underside of the vertical stabilizer. A second HF radio antenna cable is mounted between two posts on the fuselage underside below the main cabin. Small radar warning receiver antennas are mounted on either side of the nose, on the outboard weapons pylons, and wing end plates.

After a short period of operational tests and deployment further improvements were made to the Hind D. The Laser designator pod was repositioned from the port inboard pylon to the tip of the port stub wing, additional low speed precision airflow sensors were fitted on the air data sensor boom and the short wave aerial cable under the tail boom was deleted.

During 1979, the engine air intakes were fitted with vortex dust/debris extractors to prevent engine ingestion of foreign objects during ground operation, takeoff, landing and while in a low hover. During this same timeframe the Soviets changed the tactical markings carried on the Hind D. The unit tactical number, usually the last two digits of the serial number, was repositioned from the nose behind the cockpit to the rear fuselage behind the national insignia.

Warsaw Pact pilots who converted from the Hip (Mi-8) to the Hind (Mi-24) reported that the Hind's cockpit is more cramped than the Hip and there are more instruments and switches to handle. With a shorter control stick the Hind is more sensitive, however, the Hind has better climb, speed, and a greater combat radius. The flight characteristics

The bulge under the fuselage behind the sensor packs on this early production Hind D is the semi-retractable nose wheel. The wires running from the fuselage to the horizontal stabilizers are HF radio antennas. Yellow 07 is camouflaged in Light Brown, Medium Brown upper surfaces over Light Blue undersurfaces.

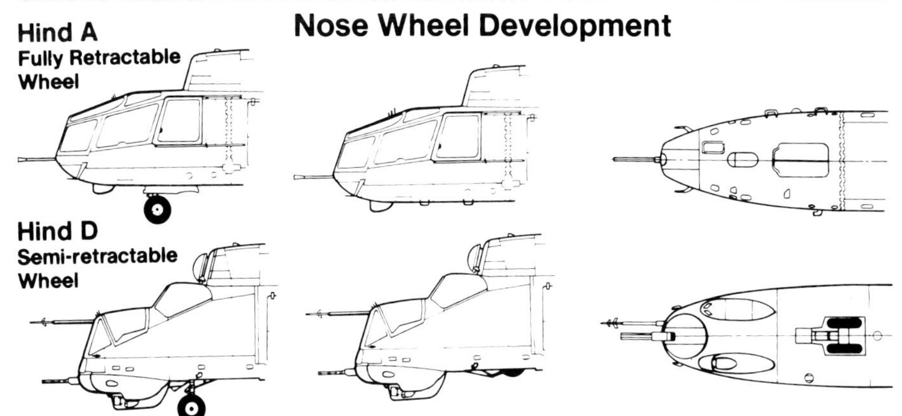

The UB-32 rocket pods on this early Hind D are fitted with a rocket exhaust deflectors on the back of the pod to protect the underside of the stub wing when the rockets are fired. The small downward angled pipe on the fuselage behind the rotor is the Auxiliary Power Unit (APU) exhaust.

of the Hind are more demanding than the Hip, but in the hands of an experienced pilot the gunship is a maneuverable, highly efficient weapons system.

Crew training for the Hind is extensive, especially for the weapons system operator. The Swatter (AT-2) missiles are command radio guided and controlled with a small joy stick in the WSO's cockpit. The missile must be visually tracked to the target requiring a great deal of skill and training to become proficient in guiding the missile.

A senior Soviet officer was recently quoted on the capabilities and mission of the Hind D: *"The attack helicopter will probably have as great an impact in some future war as the tank had in the Great Patriotic War (World War II). The Stromovick helicopter plays an important role in difficult terrain, such as jungles and mountains, and it could prove equally important during fighting in the sprawling cities of Europe and Asia, in fact, anywhere."*

Again using the designation A-10, a modified Hind D was used by the Soviets to capture a World's helicopter speed record. On 21 September 1978 test pilot Gurgen R. Karapetyan flew the A-10 over a 9.32 by 15 by 53 mile closed course at a speed of 228.9 mph. The A-10 (Hind D) was prepared for the record attempt by removing all armament, armor, and pylons.

The Hind D was exported to all Warsaw Pact countries except Romania. For export the gunships are dismantled at the factory and shipped to the country of destination in specially designed crates. Upon arrival the helicopters are re-assembled and test flown by a factory test pilot, before being turned over to their new owners. Unverified reports state that the Soviet Union grants a two year warranty on all aviation equipment exported to Warsaw Pact countries.

The Soviets have continued to improve the Hind D and from 1982 to 1985 a number of changes were noted on service Hind Ds. The UHF aerial mast on the top of the tail boom was redesigned and a chaff/flare dispenser was fitted on the underside of the tail boom near the horizontal stabilizer. Infrared counter measures (IRCM) pulsed jammers were introduced, however, in many cases although the faired platform at the rear of the

A flight of Soviet Air Force Hind Ds prepare to land. The windows on the fuselage side can be locked open in flight and are equipped with mounts for AK-47 assault rifles. The four barreled 12.7MM gatling gun nose turret can engage targets up to sixty degrees on either side.

Rocket Pod Exhaust Shield

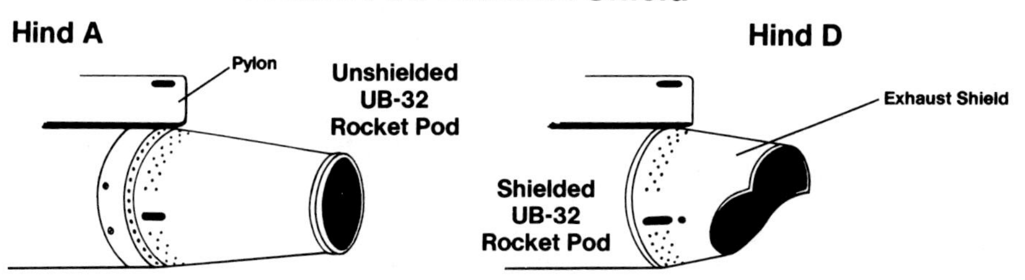

A flight of Polish Air Force Hind Ds, White 15 and 16, during the Spring of 1981. The factory applied camouflage patterns are slightly different, a common feature of Russian built aircraft. Standard factory patterns vary from aircraft to aircraft and colors differ in shade depending on the paint mix.

The strong rotor downwash in a low hover causes debris to be thrown up into the engine intakes. During 1979 the Soviets began fitting Hind Ds with vortex dust/debris extractors to protect the engines. The large engine exhausts produce a high infrared signature making the Hind vulnerable to heat seeking missiles.

Vortex Dust/Debris Extractors

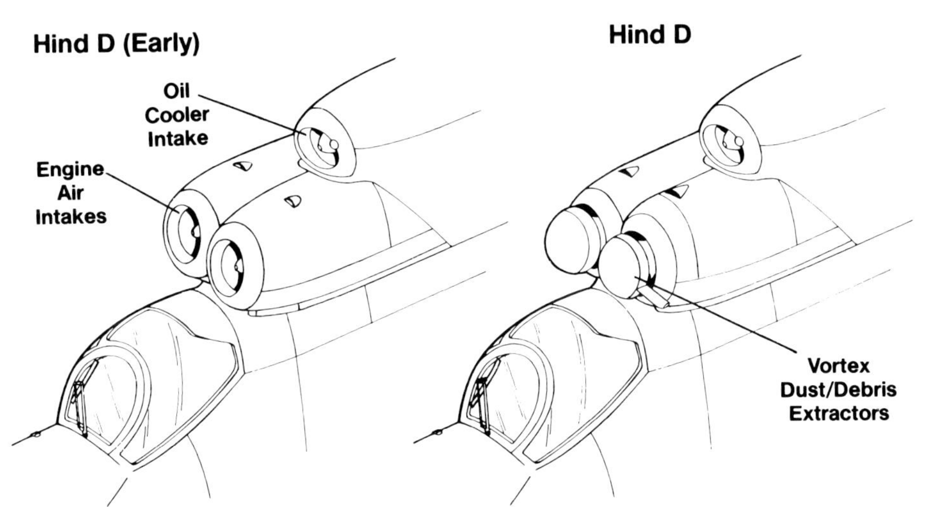

A pair of Soviet Air Force Hind Ds climb out for a training mission. The Hind in the foreground is carrying two Swatter (AT-2) anti-tank guided missiles on the wing end plate pylons.

engine cover fairing was installed the IRCM jammers themselves were not carried. A number of late production Hind Ds have been noted with more tapered and pointed tail rotor blades. The air data sensor boom cover, which prevents damage to the sensors on the ground, was also redesigned.

During 1986 Western analysts detected still further refinements to Hind Ds in Europe. The angle of the exhausts were changed to allow installation of infrared suppression exhaust mixers. To date the IR suppression units have been noted on Hind Ds destined for use in Afghanistan and Nicaragua where the presence of American made Stinger shoulder launched infrared homing anti-aircraft missiles present a serious threat. An unidentified sensor has been added on each side of the nose below the

A Hind D of the Czechslovakian Air Force takes off as a MiG-23BN Flogger F flies overhead. This Hind carries an enhanced low speed air data boom that supplies precision air speed data to the fire control computer. The Czechs have at least twenty-eight Hind Ds with a number of them based at Plzen-Dobrany close to the West German border.

APU Exhaust

Hind A

Upturned Exhaust Port

Hind D

Downturned Exhaust Port

weapons operator's cockpit and what is believed to be a tail warning radar antenna was installed on the rear of the vertical stabilizer. Most of these modifications were introduced on the production line at both Arsenyev and Rostov, and kits were produced to allow early production Hind Ds to be retro-fitted with them during major overhauls.

A dedicated trainer variant was also developed for the Hind D. This variant had the nose gun and air data boom deleted and the turret faired over. This training variant of the Hind D is believed to be a pilot trainer without the complex weapons systems, with the forward cockpit used by the instructor while the student sits in the rear cockpit. Student weapons systems operators are trained in standard, fully equipped Hind Ds.

During maintenance the Swatter missile rails, UB-32 pods, nose gun, pitot tubes, and sensor boom are covered. The oil cooler intake cover and Laser designator lens cap are Red with White numbers. The White stripes on the Black main rotor blades are the electrical deicing system.

Polish maintenance personnel work on the main rotor hub of a Polish Air Force Mi-2 Hoplite while a Hind D is inspected by another crew in the background. The Hind D appears to be relatively new and carries the last two digits of the serial number (1014) in White on the tail boom.

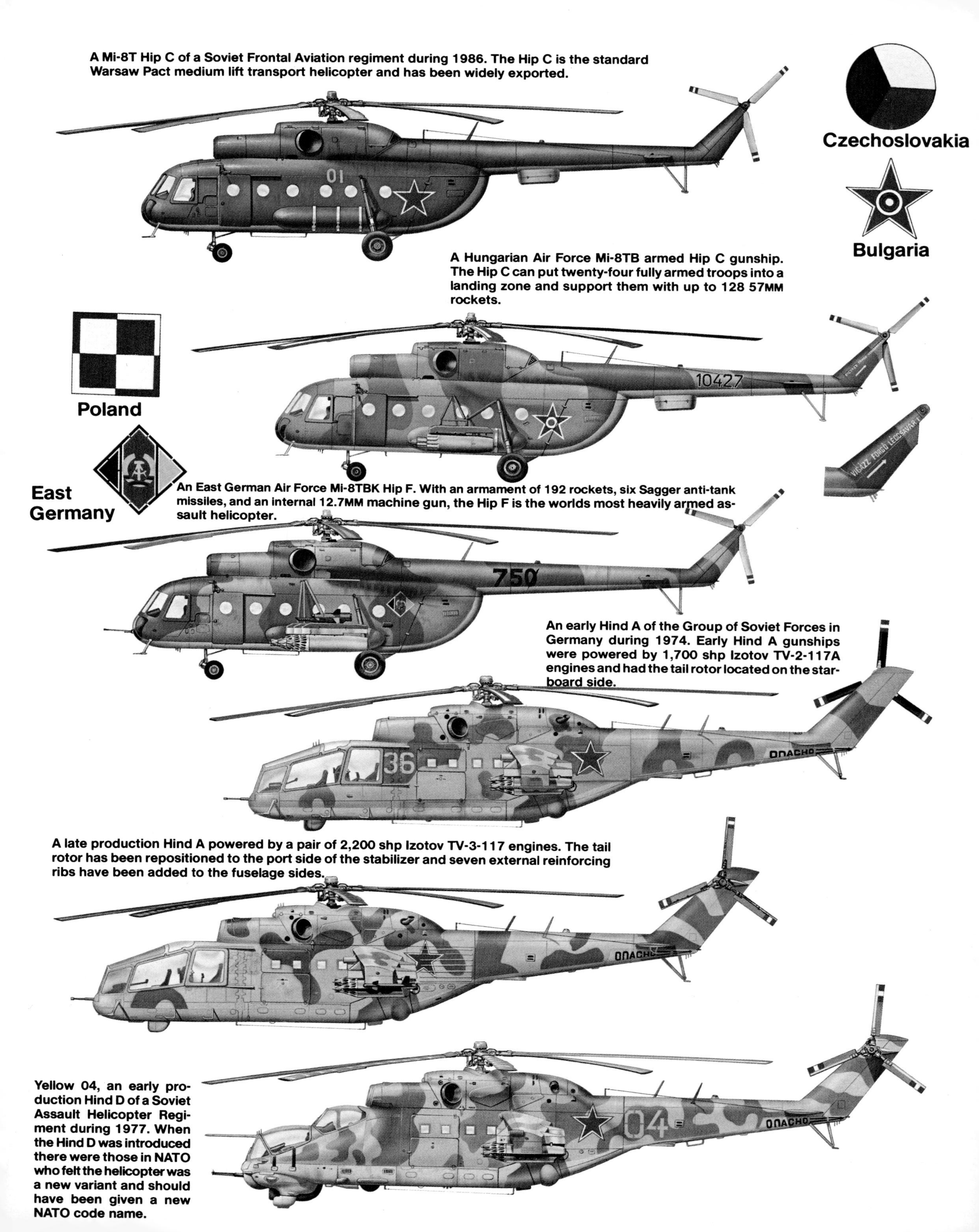

A Mi-8T Hip C of a Soviet Frontal Aviation regiment during 1986. The Hip C is the standard Warsaw Pact medium lift transport helicopter and has been widely exported.

A Hungarian Air Force Mi-8TB armed Hip C gunship. The Hip C can put twenty-four fully armed troops into a landing zone and support them with up to 128 57MM rockets.

An East German Air Force Mi-8TBK Hip F. With an armament of 192 rockets, six Sagger anti-tank missiles, and an internal 12.7MM machine gun, the Hip F is the worlds most heavily armed assault helicopter.

An early Hind A of the Group of Soviet Forces in Germany during 1974. Early Hind A gunships were powered by 1,700 shp Izotov TV-2-117A engines and had the tail rotor located on the starboard side.

A late production Hind A powered by a pair of 2,200 shp Izotov TV-3-117 engines. The tail rotor has been repositioned to the port side of the stabilizer and seven external reinforcing ribs have been added to the fuselage sides.

Yellow 04, an early production Hind D of a Soviet Assault Helicopter Regiment during 1977. When the Hind D was introduced there were those in NATO who felt the helicopter was a new variant and should have been given a new NATO code name.

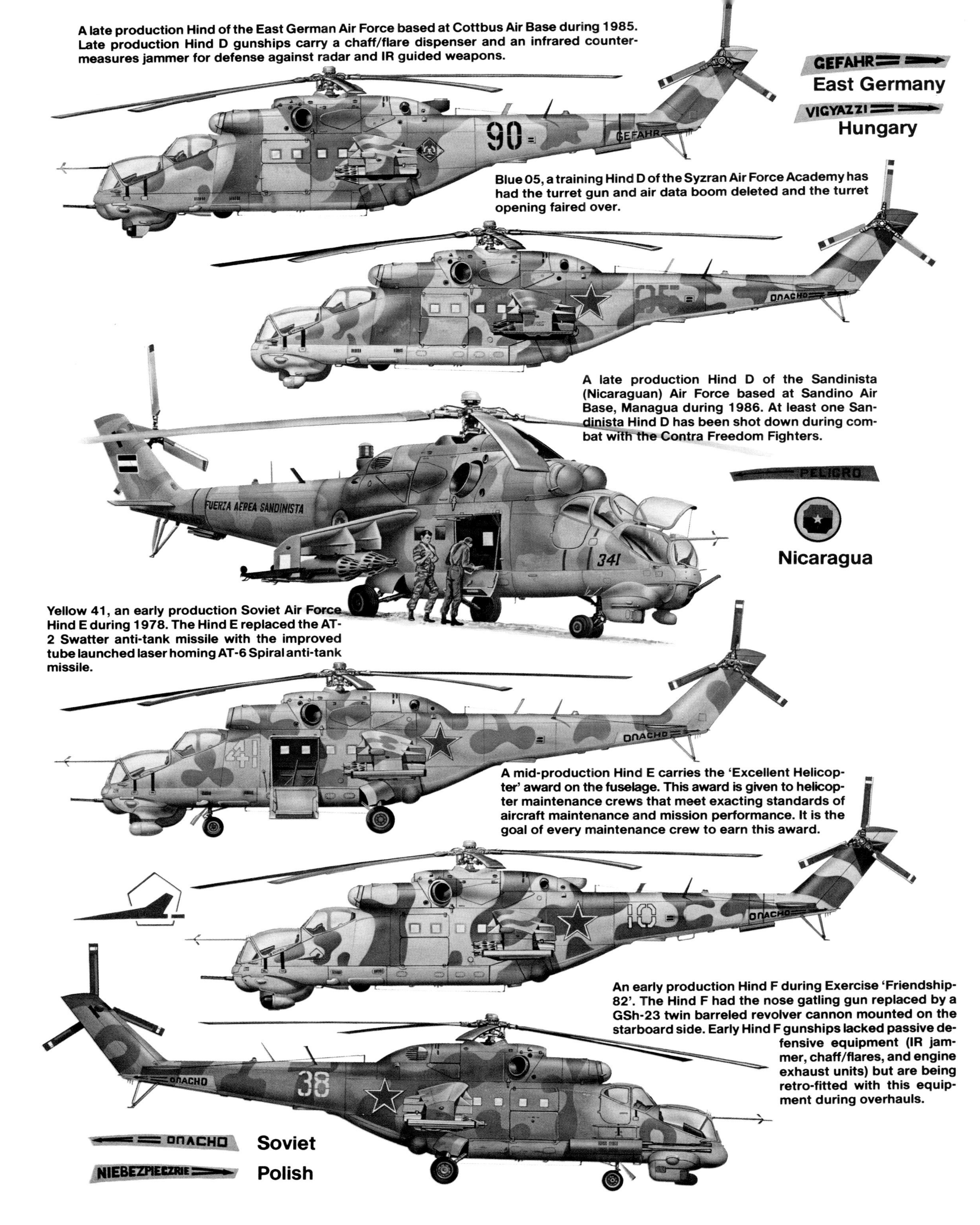

A late production Hind of the East German Air Force based at Cottbus Air Base during 1985. Late production Hind D gunships carry a chaff/flare dispenser and an infrared countermeasures jammer for defense against radar and IR guided weapons.

Blue 05, a training Hind D of the Syzran Air Force Academy has had the turret gun and air data boom deleted and the turret opening faired over.

A late production Hind D of the Sandinista (Nicaraguan) Air Force based at Sandino Air Base, Managua during 1986. At least one Sandinista Hind D has been shot down during combat with the Contra Freedom Fighters.

Yellow 41, an early production Soviet Air Force Hind E during 1978. The Hind E replaced the AT-2 Swatter anti-tank missile with the improved tube launched laser homing AT-6 Spiral anti-tank missile.

A mid-production Hind E carries the 'Excellent Helicopter' award on the fuselage. This award is given to helicopter maintenance crews that meet exacting standards of aircraft maintenance and mission performance. It is the goal of every maintenance crew to earn this award.

An early production Hind F during Exercise 'Friendship-82'. The Hind F had the nose gatling gun replaced by a GSh-23 twin barreled revolver cannon mounted on the starboard side. Early Hind F gunships lacked passive defensive equipment (IR jammer, chaff/flares, and engine exhaust units) but are being retro-fitted with this equipment during overhauls.

Polish Hind crews receive last minute instructions before manning their aircraft. During exercises crews often are briefed on the exact location of the 'target' by radio while in the air enroute to the target area. Serial 1015 is believed to have been built in 1979 and was one of the first group of Hinds delivered to Poland.

The enhanced low speed air data boom carries precision airflow sensors that feed information to the Hind's weapons aiming computer. A three pole Odd Rods (SRD-2M) IFF antenna is mounted on the boom attachment point on the canopy frame.

A late production Hind D hovers over its landing pad just after takeoff. The vanes on the air data boom are the low speed sensor that provide precise information on airspeed, side forces, and attitude changes to the fire control computer in the weapons systems operators cockpit.

Air Data Boom

Hind D (Early)

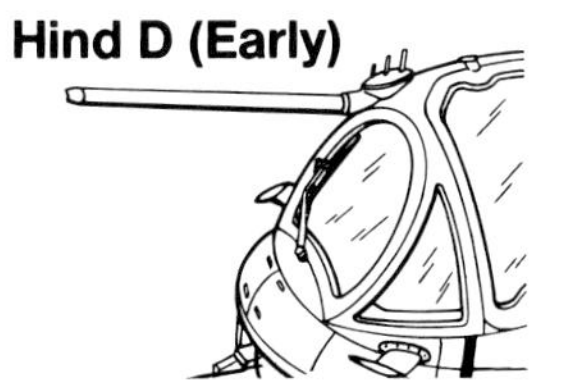

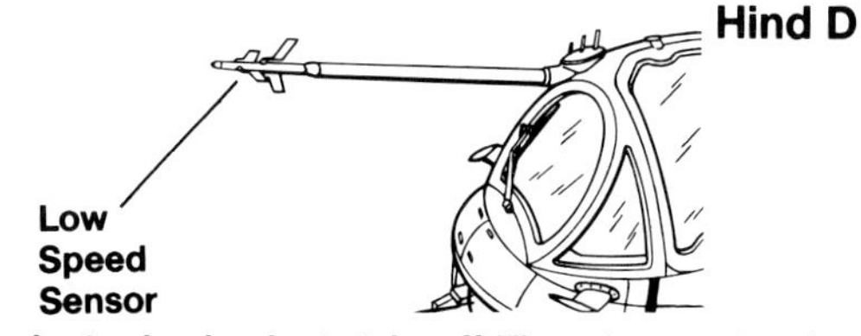

A Polish Air Force Hind D receives a last minute check prior to take off. The rotors are turning as a mechanic works in the open split doorway of the main compartment. The vehicle in the background is an Ural 375 fuel truck.

A Hind D on ground alert waits with the main cabin doors open ready to load a squad of troops. Although the Hind D can carry eight troopers, it is believed that in combat the cabin would be used to carry reloads for the Swatter missile system instead of troops.

The crew of a Hind D board their aircraft for another training mission. The laser designator pod on the port wingtip has the protective lens cap installed and is not used for routine flights or training not involving the Swatter missile system.

One of the Hind's principal advantages is that the aircraft can be easily serviced under all conditions. The engine access doors double as maintenance platforms for ground crews. The IFF antenna and air data boom sensors are protected on the ground by coverings painted in Red.

Cockpit Hatches

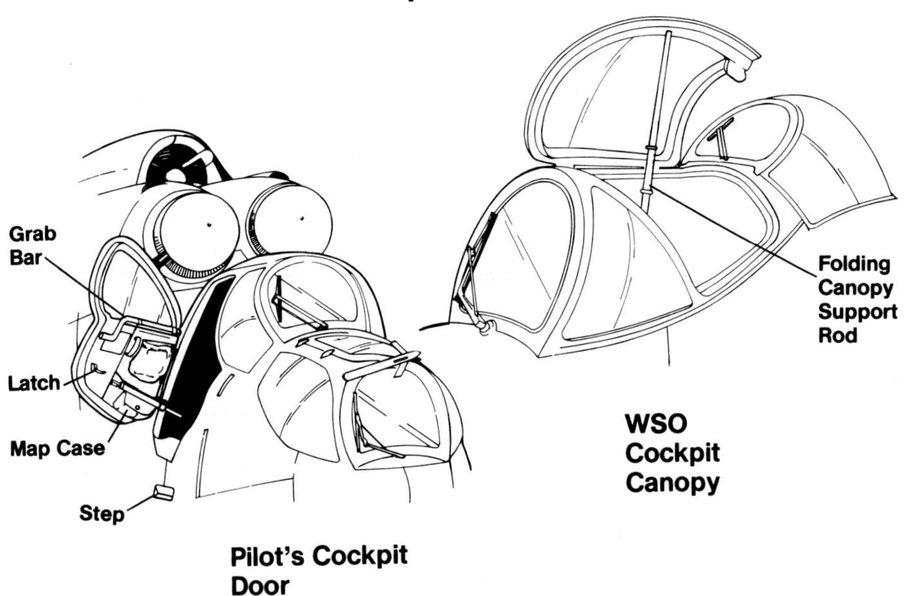

A gunship pilot climbs into the cockpit of his Hind D through the heavily armored automobile style door. Both the pilot's and WSO's windshields are equipped with different style windshield wiper blades.

The Flat Black pilot's entrance door on the Hind D is heavily armored and has a stowage bag for maps and other important documents. The Silver handle is the door locking handle and behind it is a placard explaining the locking operation.

A Polish weapons systems (WSO) operator in the cockpit of a Polish Air Force Hind D. The missile control sight is mounted on the port side of the cockpit. In 1982 crews began receiving the hard flight helmet worn by the WSO, replacing the leather helmet usually worn by helicopter crews in Warsaw Pact countries.

A Swatter (AT-2) missile streaks away from a Hind D during live fire training. The solid propellant Swatter is a radio command guided weapon with movable control surfaces on the trailing edges of its rear mounted wings. The WSO steers the missile by keeping the cross-hairs of the missile control unit on the target. The onboard missile director sends the necessary radio signals to the missile to ensure it scores a hit.

A flight of three Polish Hind Ds prepare to take off. Warsaw Pact tactics call for Hinds to operate in flights of three. The leader normally flies above and behind the two wingman to spot targets and direct the attack. White 15 is a early production Hind D with the initial UHF aerial mast, while the second gunship, White 78, is equipped with a later UHF aerial mast introduced in 1982.

An early production Hind D of the Soviet Air Force parked on a helopad in Eastern Europe. The two armored doors of the Low Light Level TV sensor are open. On the ground the Hind's main rotor blades have a distinctive droop if the helicopter is parked for any length of time. The blades are usually tied down to prevent wind damage when the helicopter is secured.

A Hind D undergoing maintenance has the doors of the Forward Looking Infrared (FLIR)/Low Light Level TV (LLTV) sensor open so the system can be calibrated. The open missile director pod is wired into test equipment as the technician checks its operation. The radar antenna itself is covered by a Red protective cover with White numbers.

Forward Looking Infrared/Low Light Level TV Sensor Pod

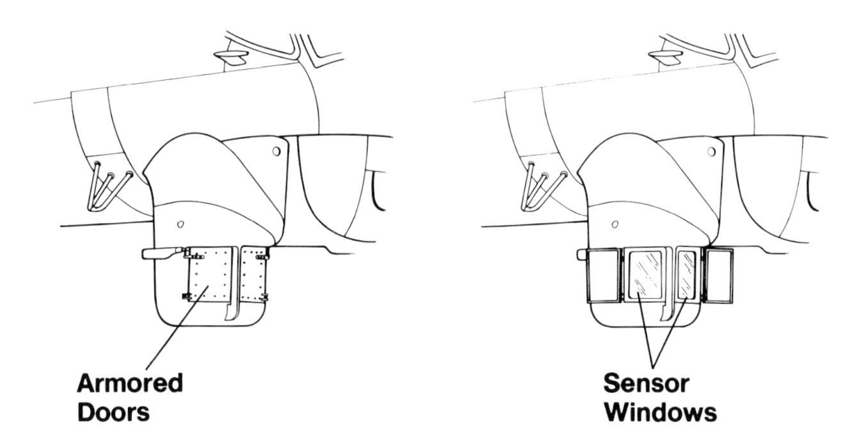

The doors above the 12.7MM gatling gun turret are the access doors for the ammunition bay. It is believed that the bay holds 500 rounds of belted 12.7MM ammunition. The small box to the right of the gun is the setscrew control for adjusting the boresight of the turret.

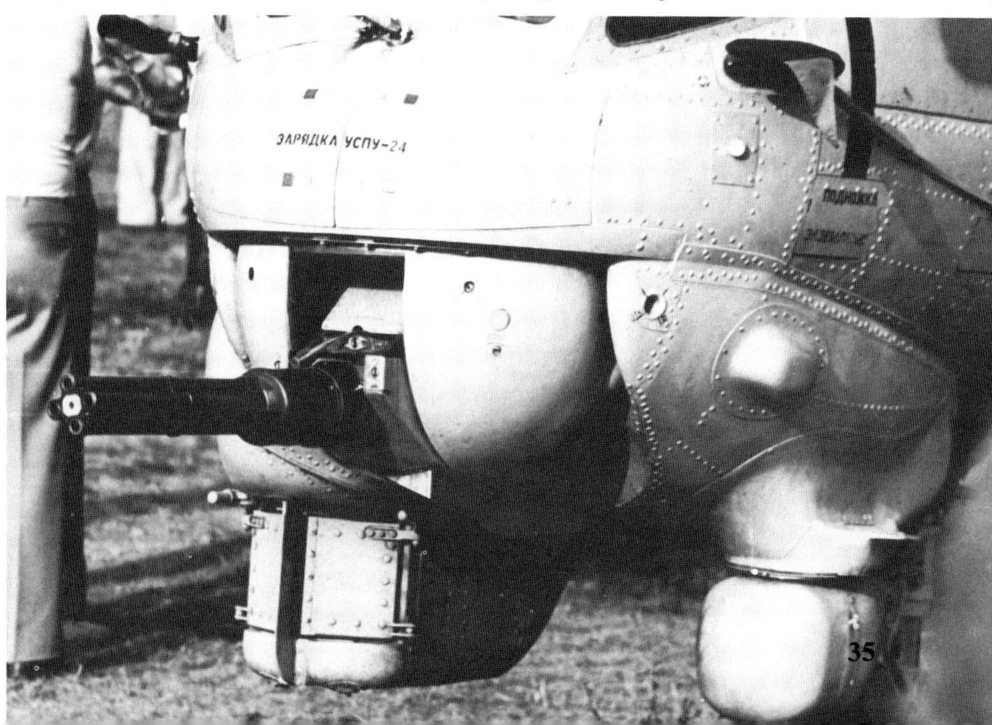

A pair of Polish Hind Ds in trail formation during 1981. Swatter anti-tank missiles are usually not carried on routine training missions. Both Hinds are equipped with the later style UHF radio antenna on the top of the tail boom.

Upper Tail Boom Antennas

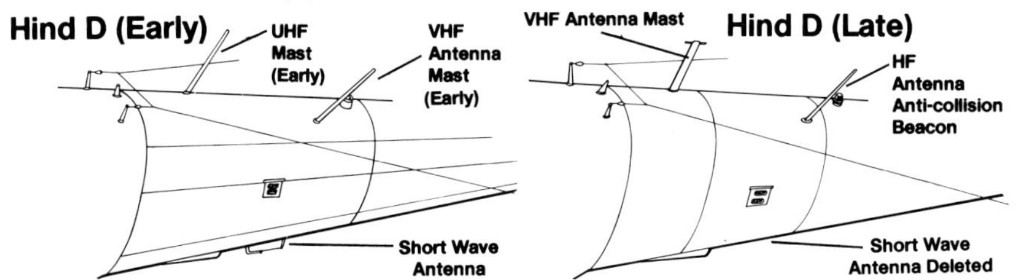

Because of the distinctive shape of the double canopys, the Hind D was named *Gorbach* (Hunchback) by its Warsaw Pact crews. The Black areas on the fuselage side and upper stub wing are exhaust stains from the engine exhaust.

White 74 a late production Hind D of the Polish Air Force hovers over its landing site at a Polish airfield. The three Hinds all have minor differences in their camouflage patterns. White 78 is equipped with the later style cross shaped air data sensor cover, while White 13 is fitted with the older round cover.

(Above) A Hind D of the German Democratic Republic Air Force on a training flight over East Germany. Hind Ds of the *Luftstreitkräfte* were first shown to the German public when they took part in a fly-by during the 30th anniversary celebrations of the formation of the German Democratic Republic held in East Berlin on 7 October 1979.

(Below) A late production Hind D of the Czechsolvakian Air Force has the late style UHF antenna. The small dome shaped object behind the raked VHF antenna on the tail boom is the Red anti-collision rotating beacon.

Ground crews perform routine maintenance on a Hind D. The crewman in the foreground is fitting an early style protective cover to the low speed sensors on the air data boom. The time between overhauls on Soviet helicopters is much lower than on their Western counterparts.

A ground crewman has removed the air data sensor cover from the air data boom during a preflight check. This is the late cross shaped sensor cover first introduced in 1982 to replace the earlier round cover that was found to be difficult to use in service. The White number '74' on the Red cover matches the aircraft side number '74'.

A ground crewman opens the starboard engine cover on a late production Hind D. All sensitive equipment: IFF antenna, low speed sensors, pitot tubes, pilot's windshield wiper, and laser designator have been fitted with covers to protect them during servicing and while the aircraft is parked.

Air Data Boom Sensor Covers

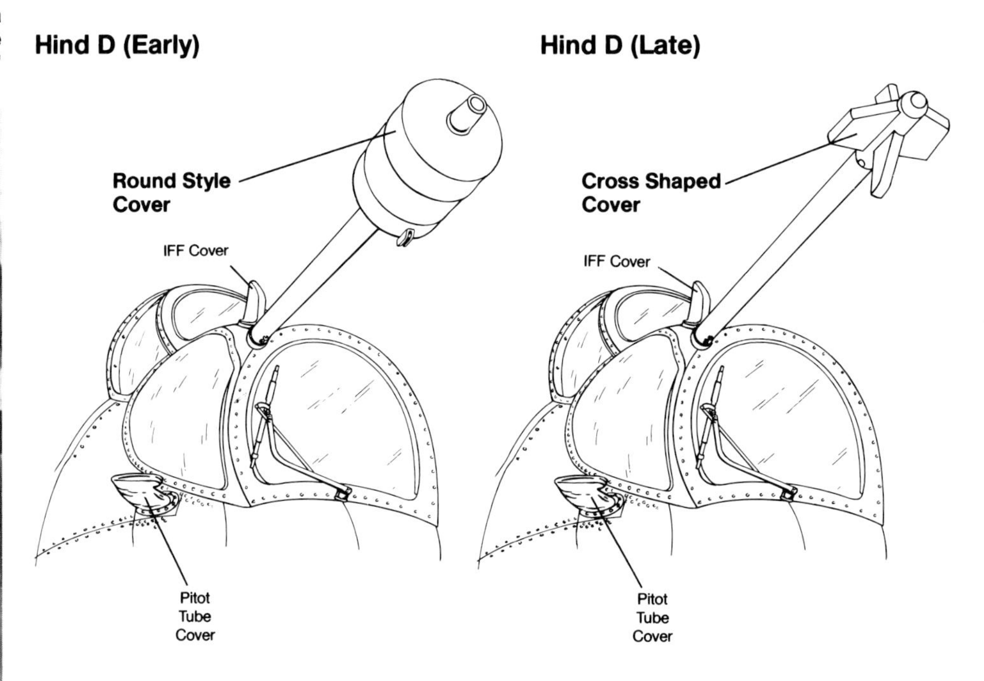

A Polish Air Force Hind D lifts off a fog shrouded airfield in Eastern Europe past a line of Mi-4 Hounds in the background. The nose down attitude of the Hind is typical of a helicopter in transition from vertical to horizontal flight.

East German troops camouflage a pair of Hind Ds with netting in a wooded area near the Baltic coast during the Warsaw Pact exercise *Sojuz 81* held in late March of 1981. The canopies have been covered with tarps to prevent sunlight from reflecting off the canopy glass.

An East German Hind D lifts off to escort three Hip Fs (Mi-8TBK) from Cottbus Air Base during an exercise in May of 1981. Black 417 carries an unusual weapons load, a single UB-32 rocket pod on the inboard starboard stub wing pylon. The two small round antennas in front of the tail skid are the transmitter and receiver antennas for the RV-5 radio altimeter.

A Czech Hind D climbs out of a wooded meadow. The tactical number 0103 is in Black with a thin White outline. The Cyrillic 'Danger' inscription on the lower tail boom is Black on a Yellow background. Czechoslovakia is one of the few Warsaw Pact countries which did not change the Russian warning for one in their own language.

(Above and Below) White 15 and White 76 of the Polish Air Force reveal one of the subtle changes that help identify Hind Ds built in successive production blocks. White 15 is believed to have been produced in 1979 and has the early style UHF antenna on the upper starboard side of the tail boom, while White 76 was produced during late 1982 or early 1983 and has the later style UHF antenna. The camouflage schemes also differ slightly.

A late production Hind D begins a rolling takeoff from a taxiway during an exercise in late August of 1985. The rugged undercarrage of the Hind D allows the aircraft to make short rolling takeoffs when fully loaded with weapons, fuel, and troops.

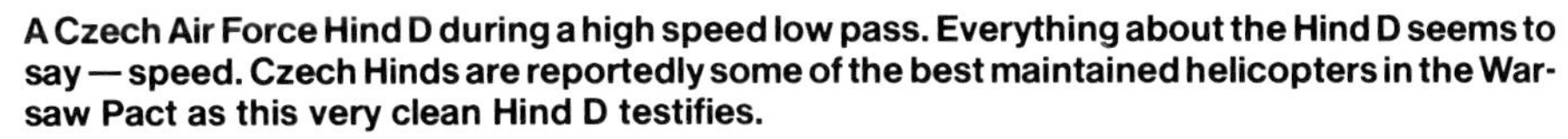

A Czech Air Force Hind D during a high speed low pass. Everything about the Hind D seems to say — speed. Czech Hinds are reportedly some of the best maintained helicopters in the Warsaw Pact as this very clean Hind D testifies.

A formation of Hind Ds of the Polish Air Force during 1985. White 77 is a 1982 production model with the later style UHF antenna. The second aircraft, White 57, is a late production Hind D with chaff/flare dispenser and IRCM jammer. White 13 is the oldest Hind D, delivered to Poland in 1979. White 58 is also a late production Hind D.

White 58, a late production Hind D of the Polish Air Force carries both the IRCM jammer and chaff/flare dispenser. The chaff/flare dispenser is a strap on unit which is secured to the tail boom between the tall skid and radio altimeter antenna with two metal bands.

IRCM Jammer

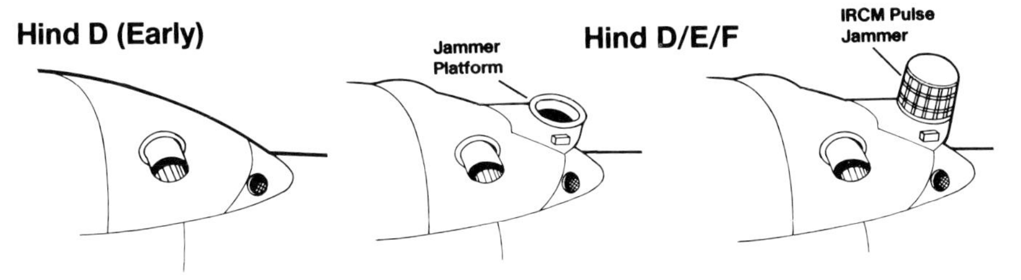

The late style UHF antenna and IRCM jammer platform identify this as a late production Hind D. Although the platform for the IRCM jammer is fitted, the jammer itself is not carried. This is a common practice on late Hind Ds in Warsaw Pact service.

(Above and Below) The weapons system operator and flight engineer check the inboard Swatter (AT-2) missile rack on an East German late production Hind D while other ground crewmen carry ammunition boxes to the waiting Hind. Reloading the weapons systems on any helicopter while the engines are running is a difficult task. The crewman by the open door is plugged into the Hind's intercom and can communicate the progress of the weapons loading to the pilot. The running lights are part of the MLOK-P/R-15 runway lighting system.

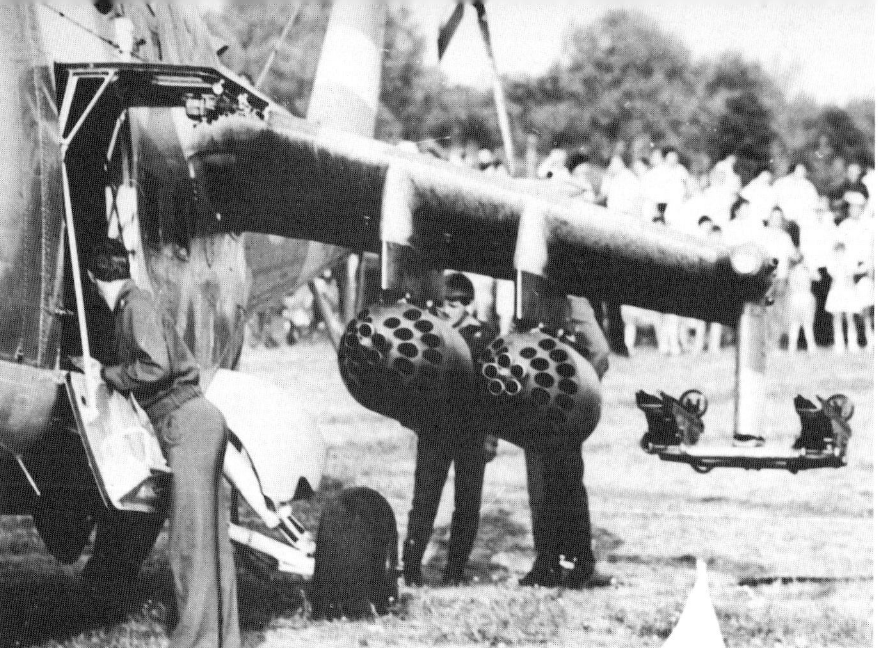

A spectator examines the cabin of a Hind D at an airshow in Eastern Europe. The interior of the Hind is painted in Light Gray. The 'U' shaped handles attached to the boarding step are grab handles to help close the door from the inside of the cabin.

Cabin Door

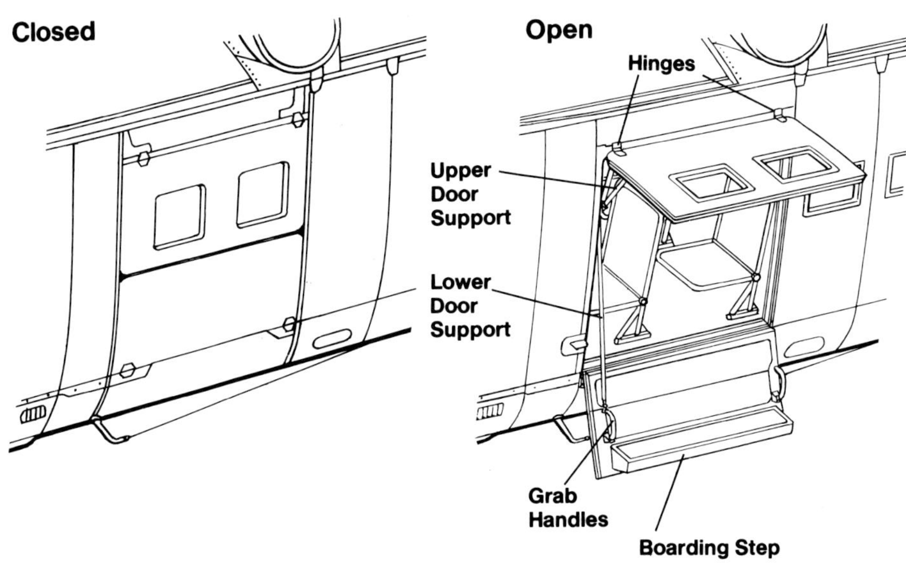

(Above) A Hungarian Air Force Hind D carries a chaff/flare dispenser and provision for an infrared countermeasures pulsed jammer. The chaff/flare dispenser was introduced on service Hind Ds during 1985.

(Below) East German troops board a late production Hind D during exercises in 1985. Black 90 is equipped with the later style UHF antenna first introduced in 1982. A chaff/flare dispenser is mounted under the tail boom in front of the tail skid and a mounting platform for an infrared jammer is installed on the rear of the APU fairing.

The strong rotor downwash of the Hind in a low hover was one of the factors that resulted in the introduction of the vortex dust/debris separators on the engine air intakes. The separators do, however, reduce engine airflow by some ten percent lowering available engine power at low speeds.

A Hind D of the Hungarian Air Force carries the chaff/flare dispenser on the underside of the tail boom just in front of the tail skid. Chaff/flares are carried to confuse anti-aircraft radars (chaff) and to decoy infrared homing missiles (flares). These units are being retrofitted to older Hind D's during major overhauls.

The new exhaust stubs were fitted to older Hind D's during regular overhauls. In addition to forcing the exhaust gasses upwards, the new exhausts may be fitted with IR suppression cool air mixers, although these are rarely seen except on Hinds stationed in combat zones.

Engine Exhausts

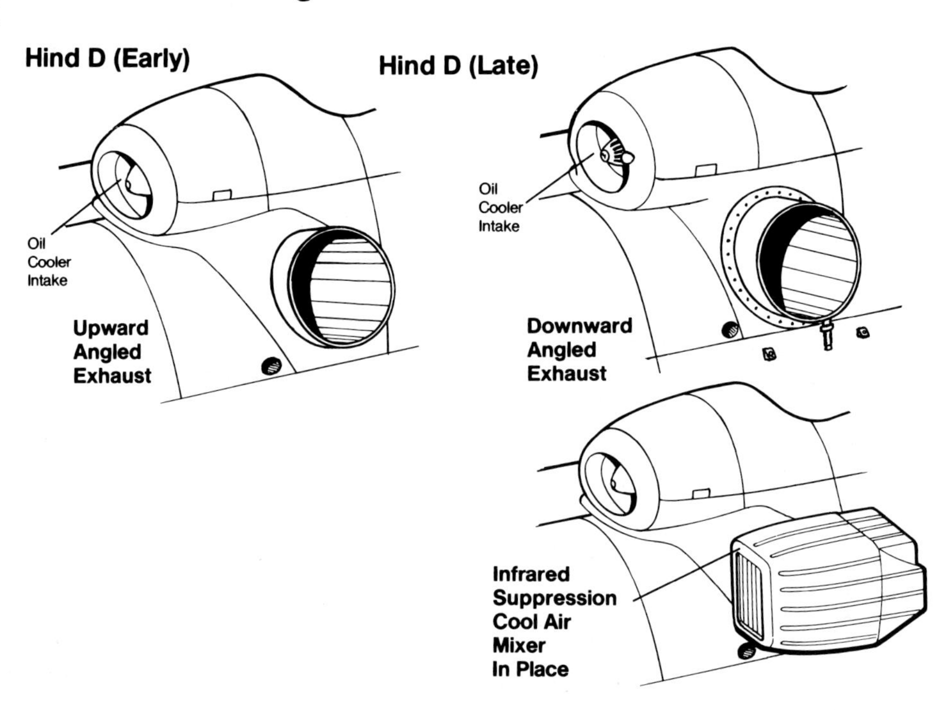

(Above)Although equipped with the IRCM jammer platform, the jammer unit itself is not carried on this Hungarian Air Force Hind D. This Hind has been modified with the new exhaust stubs and carries a chaff/flare dispenser on the tail boom. The side number is Red outlined with a thin White border.

(Below)This pair of Hind Ds are believed to be two of the first Hinds delivered to Poland in October of 1979. The last two digits of the serial number (1015 and 1016) are carried on the tail boom in White. The Polish Air Force operates three Hind squadrons named ***Berezyna***, ***Karpaty***, and ***Tarcza***.

A Hungarian Air Force Hind D fitted with new sensor pods on the nose under the weapons systems operator's cockpit. Some sources believe that the sensors may be used for helicopter vs helicopter air combat, while others believe that they are associated with a passive infrared system.

As its ground crew stands by a Hungarian Air Force Hind D prepares to take off. The Hind carries a single UB-32 rocket pod on the outboard wing pylon and an Swatter (AT-2) missile on the inner missile rail. The lower portion of the wing pylons and the UB-32 pod are in Silver-Gray.

Nose Sensor

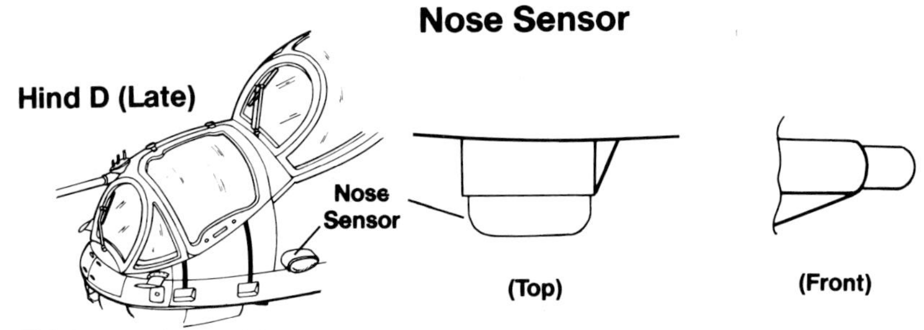

This late production Hind D carries two new sensor pods on each side of the nose below the WSO's cockpit. These sensors were first introduced on the Hind during 1985, however, their purpose is yet unknown to Western analysts.

Strap-on Chaff/Flare Dispenser

A late production Hind D fitted with modified upward angled exhaust stubs, nose sensors and chaff/flare dispenser. These modifications are intended to improve the Hind's survivability by reducing the risk from enemy defensive weapons such as radar directed guns and IR homing missiles.

A Soviet ground crewman loads an ammunition belt into the four barreled 12.7MM gatling gun of a Hind D. The four barreled gun can fire 800 rounds per minute. The open door above the crewman's head is the access door for the ammunition bay.

The pilot of a Soviet Hind D performs final checks before taking off for another training mission. The nose wheel of the Hind is fully steerable making the Hind very maneuverable on the ground. The turret gatling gun is at its fully elevated position. The doors above the gun are the ammunition bay loading doors.

The pilot and the weapon systems operator confer before the start of another mission. The cable dangling from the WSO's leather flight helmet is the SPU-7 intercom plug. The cockpit canopy is operated manually and is hinged on the starboard side. When not in use the canopy support rod is secured to the inside canopy frame.

This Hind D of the Polish Air Force is equipped with a pulsed infrared countermeasures jammer on a platform at the rear of the APU fairing. The pulsed jammer is one of several modifications designed to lower the Hinds vulnerability to shoulder launched heat seeking missiles such as the US Stinger.

The air data sensor boom has been deleted on this Hind D used in the training role. The Hind pilot training course is reportedly three years long, conducted at both the Saratov Training Center and a school in Central Soviet Asia. The weapon operator's compartment on training Hind Ds is used by the instructor pilot while the student flys the helicopter from the rear (pilots) cockpit.

A formation of trainer Hind Ds of the Syzran Air Force Academy at Saratov. Syzran was the Military Glider Aircraft Pilot's School until 1954 when the school was disestablished and the facility became the Soviet's main training base for rotary winged aircraft. Pilots graduating from the Syzran Air Academy are reportedly among the best trained pilots in the Soviet Air Force.

Training Hind Ds of the Syzran Air Force Academy at Saratov undergo routine maintenance. The nose gun and the ammunition doors have been faired over and the air data sensor boom has been deleted. The majority of training Hinds were converted from standard Hind Ds and Hind Es.

Trainer Nose

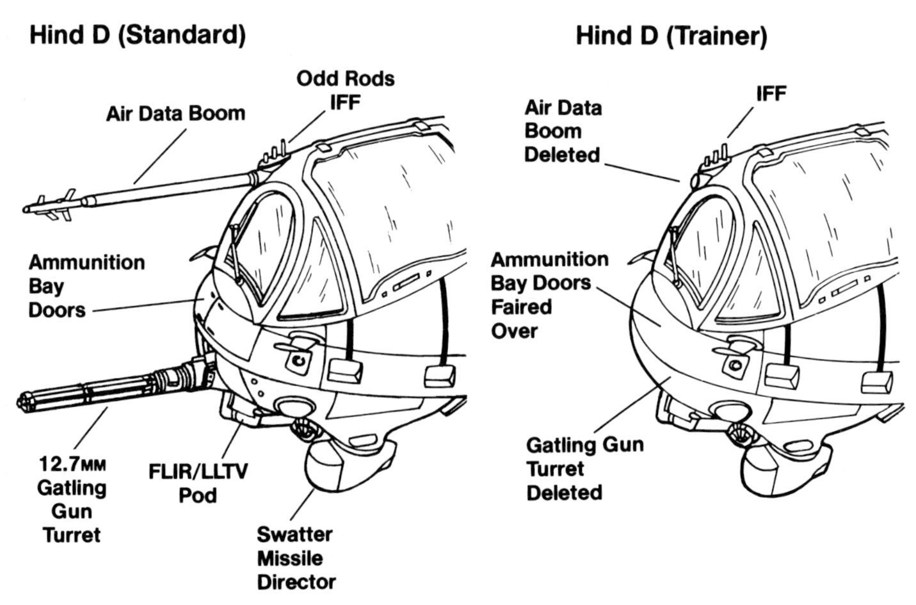

Hind D Export (Mi-25)

It is a common practice for the Soviets to offer a slightly degraded (and cheaper) export variant of their first line combat aircraft and the Hind has been no exception. The export variant of the basic Hind D was developed for export to favored nations outside the Warsaw Pact under the designation Mi-25. The Mi-25 is believed to have degraded sensors and changes in the avionics and other equipment. However, nations within the Warsaw Pack: Bulgaria, Czechoslovakia, East Germany, Hungary, and Poland operate standard Hind Ds. The following countries have received the Mi-25:

Afghanistan	Algeria	Angola
Cuba	Ethiopia	India
Iraq	Cambodia	North Korea
Libya	Nicaragua	Peru
South Yemen	Syria	Yemen
Vietnam		

Additionally two Mi-25s were captured by the Pakistani Army when their Afghani crews defected during late 1985. These aircraft are believed to remain in Pakistan where they have been thoroughly inspected and test flown by both Pakisani and Western aircrews. In April of 1987 Chad captured three Libyan Mi-24s at Wadi Doum, one of these gunships was later reportedly shipped to the United States.

Approximately 2,000 Hind Ds were built before the production of the D was phased out in 1986. Although no longer in production, the Hind D will remain in service for the foreseeable future, as long as the Swatter (AT-2) missile remains a front line Soviet weapon.

A Hind D of the Sandinista Air Force carries both the IRCM jammer and chaff/flare dispenser as protection from Stinger missiles beiieved to be used by the Nicaraguan Contra rebels. At least one Sandinista Hind is known to have been shot down.

A sharkmouthed Hind D of *Grupo Aero* 3, Peruvian Air Force. Peru operates a single squadron of Mi-25 Export Hind Ds based at Jorge Chavez Air Base outside Lima.

An Afghani Air Force Hind D carries the tail warning inscription in English. Afghan Hind Ds normally operate in mixed formations with Soviet Hinds, both for training and to ensure the Afghan crews do not defect. During 1985 two Afghan Hinds managed to elude their Soviet wingmen and landed in Pakistan.

A Syrian Air Force Hind D over the Bakka Valley in Lebanon. The Syrian roundel is carried on the fuselage sides and on the fuselage underside behind the nose wheel bay. The aircraft serial number is in Arabic characters on the tail boom in Black.

Mi-24 Hind E

To take advantage of the latest developments in anti-tank missile technology the Soviets developed, in parallel with the Swatter (AT-2) missile equipped Hind D, a modified Hind variant to mount the next generation Soviet of anti-tank weapon, the Spiral (AT-6) missile. The Spiral, operationally tested in 1974, is a tube launched, second generation radio command guided anti-tank missile with laser homing in the terminal phase of its flight. The Spiral has higher speed, greater accuracy, longer range, and an improved HEAT warhead. The missile has an effective range of 1,500 feet to approximately three miles. The Spiral is five feet ten inches long and is equipped with folding fins which unfold when the missile leaves the launch tube. The Modified Hind D was test flown during 1976, however, production was limited because of problems in the development of the Spiral missile. Production gradually increased as the Spiral completed its development phase and became an operational weapon in the Soviet inventory.

The Modified Hind D differed from the standard Hind D in armament and sensors. The missile launch rails on the wing end plates were reconfigured to accept Spiral missile tubes, a Spiral missile radar designator pod replaced the Swatter designator pod on the nose and instrument changes were made to the WSO's cockpit. The first Modified Hind Ds were similar to early production standard Hind Ds and lacked the air intake dust/debris separators and were fitted with the early style UHF antenna mast. The enhanced low speed air data boom, however, was carried. The Modified Hind D was first observed by Western analysts in East Germany during late 1979 and received the NATO code name Hind E. The Hind Es were also noted carrying a new sensor housing on the starboard side with an additional blister and aft sliding doors.

Hind Es have been updated with new equipment on approximately the same time scale as the Hind D. IRCM jammer and IR engine suppression units have been added and various communications and navigational equipment upgrades have taken place. During 1985 a change in the armament configuration was introduced on Warsaw Pact Hind Es. The two outboard pylons were equipped with missile racks to carry a pair of Spiral (AT-6) missile tubes inplace of the standard UB-32 rocket pods. In this configuration the Hind E can carry a total of eight Spiral (AT-6) missiles.

In 1986, a further modification was noted on the Hind E. Additional sensors were installed on the nose and what is believed to be a tail warning radar was installed on the vertical stabilizer. A fixed landing/search light was installed on the port side close to the nose wheel.

Except for the Spiral (AT-6) missile rails and larger missile director pod, early production Hind Es are almost identical to the Hind D from which it was developed. The Hind E first entered service with the Soviet Air Force in late 1979.

Soviet ground crews service an early production Hind E during the Winter of 1979. The Spiral (AT-6) missile rails on the wing end plate pylons and larger Spiral missile director pod on the port side of the nose are the primary identification features of the Hind E.

END Plate Missile Rails

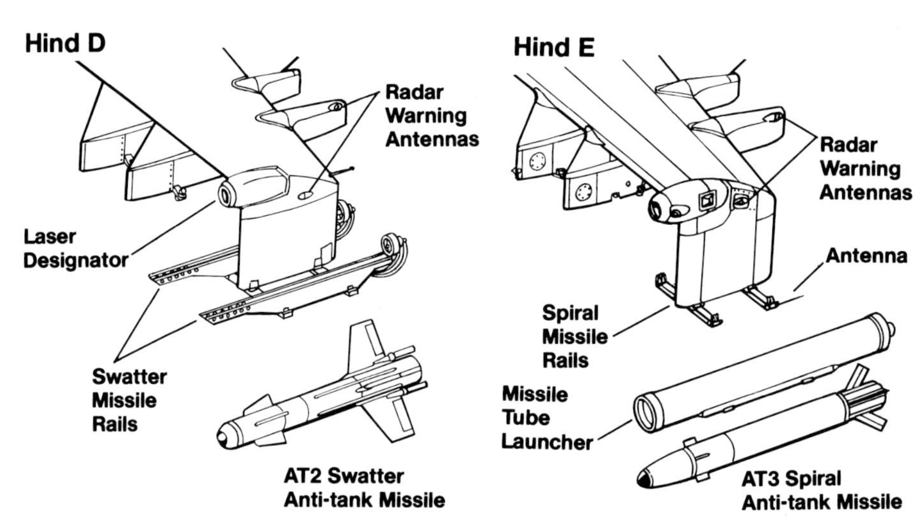

The Hind E retained the gatling gun turret of the Hind D. A Soviet armorer loads belted 12.7MM ammunition into the ammunition bay of an early Hind E. The bay holds approximately 500 rounds of belted ammunition consisting of armor piercing, incendiary and ball rounds.

The Red insignia on the nose of this Hind E is the 'Excellent Helicopter' maintenance award, carried by aircraft meeting strict maintenance standards. The award is presented to maintenance crews by a commission of high ranking officers and political commissars who decide if an aircraft or helicopter meets the exacting standards.

A ground crewman refuels an early production Hind E from a Ural fuel truck, while others inspect the nose wheel and low light TV pod. The engine and transmission access covers have been opened so that the maintenance crew can perform routine inspections of the engine, transmission and rotor head.

Missile Director Pod

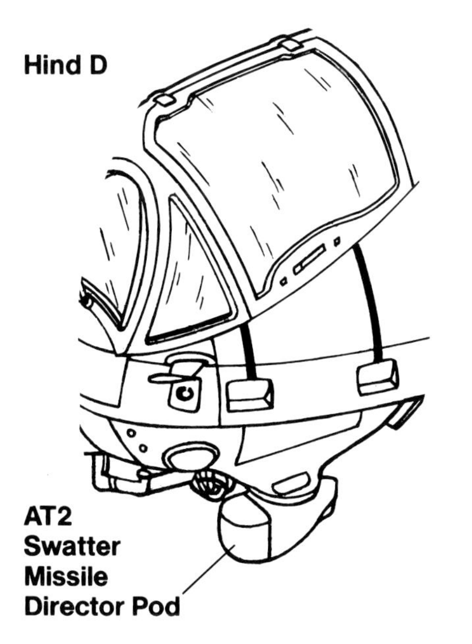

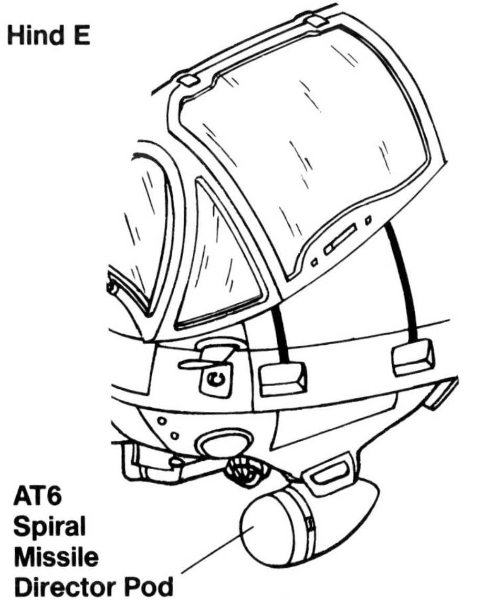

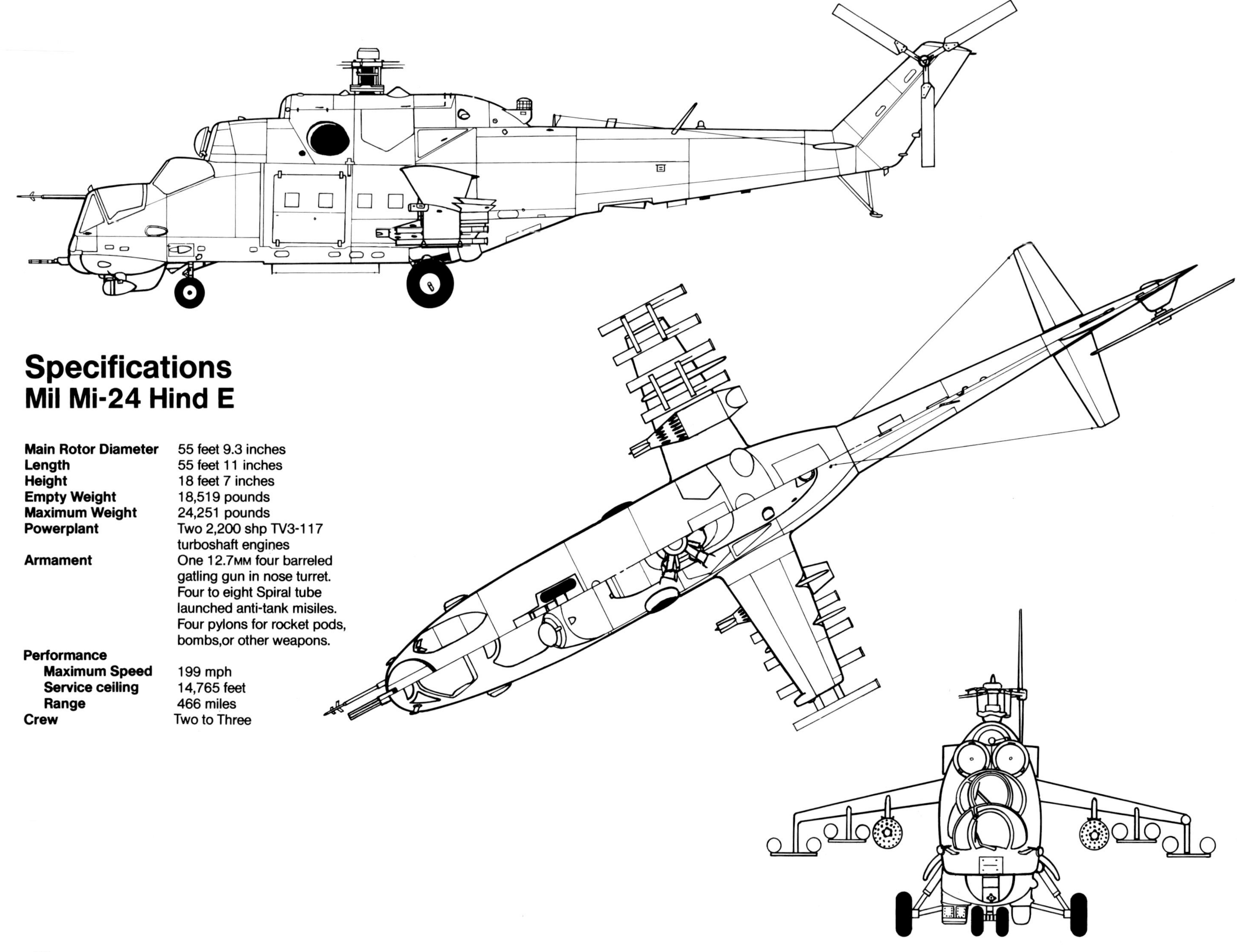

Specifications
Mil Mi-24 Hind E

Main Rotor Diameter	55 feet 9.3 inches
Length	55 feet 11 inches
Height	18 feet 7 inches
Empty Weight	18,519 pounds
Maximum Weight	24,251 pounds
Powerplant	Two 2,200 shp TV3-117 turboshaft engines
Armament	One 12.7MM four barreled gatling gun in nose turret. Four to eight Spiral tube launched anti-tank misiles. Four pylons for rocket pods, bombs,or other weapons.
Performance	
Maximum Speed	199 mph
Service ceiling	14,765 feet
Range	466 miles
Crew	Two to Three

Yellow 40, a Soviet Air Force Hind E carries Spiral (AT-6) missile tubes on the wing end plate pylons. The bulge on the nose below the pilot's canopy is a fixed search/landing light.

Hind Es prepare for takeoff on a night training flight with landing lights, position lights, and anti-collision lights brightly lit. The bright light on the nose is the landing light, position lights are mounted on the nose, wing tips, vertical stabilizer and belly. The Red anti-collision beacon is carried on the middle of the upper tail boom just behind the raked VHF antenna.

Search/Landing Light

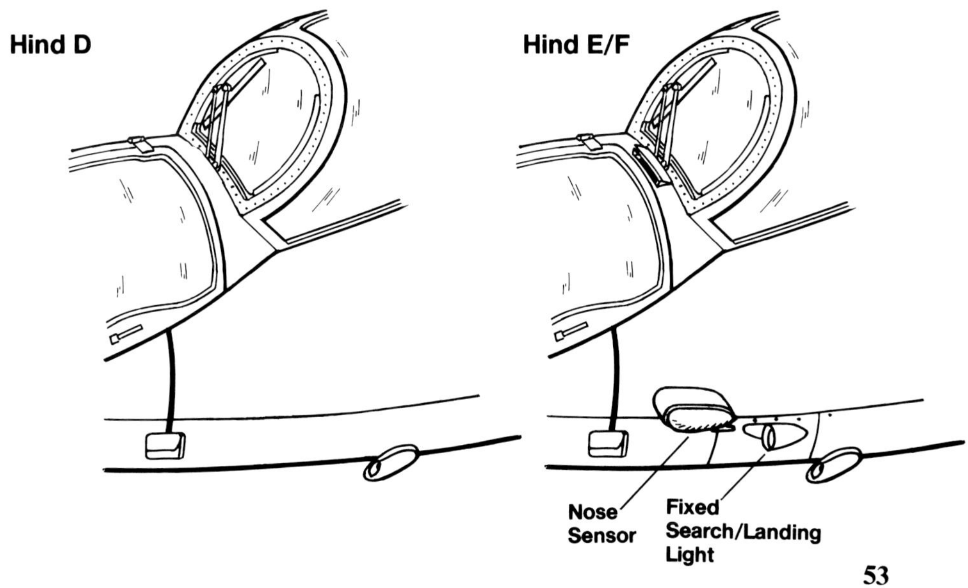

A Hungarian Air Force Hind E flies low over the countryside. This late production Hind E carries all the latest Hind modifications, nose sensors, tail warning radar, chaff/flare dispenser, IRCM jammer, and Spiral missile racks on the outboard wing pylons.

Wing Pylon Spiral Mount

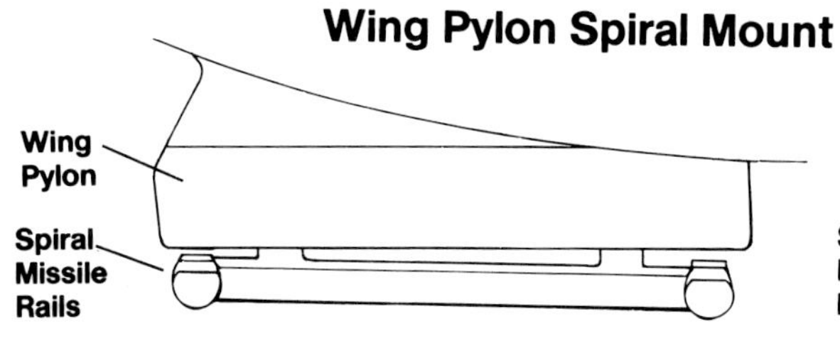

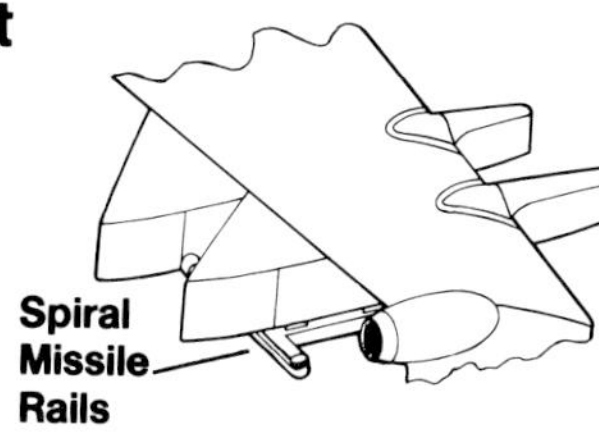

This Polish Hind E includes the latest modifications carried by Warsaw Pact Mi-24s, nose sensor, modified exhaust stubs to accomodate the Infrared Suppression Cool Air Mixers and fixed search/landing light. It is believed that the new exhausts were fitted during the Hind's last major overhaul.

Red 711, a late production Hind E is equipped with a fixed landing/search light on the port side below the nose sensor. In a combat situation the gunship would also be outfitted with infrared engine exhaust supression shields attached to the engine exhausts.

An early production Soviet Air Force Hind E flies low over the sea. The Hind carries Tan with Medium Green patches on the uppersurfaces over Light Blue undersurfaces, a camouflage scheme common to the Hind E.

A crewman peers out of the open window on the cabin door of Yellow 05, a Soviet Air Force Hind E. The Sprial (AT-6) anti-tank missile is carried in the tubes attached to the wing end plate pylons.

Tail Sensor

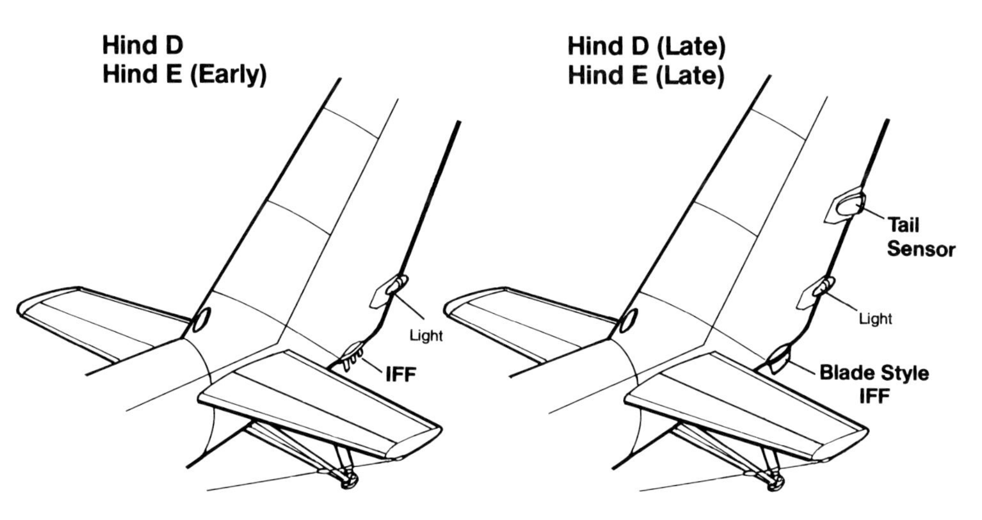

(Above) A Soviet Hind E during a low pass; the two cabin door windows appear to be open. The fixed search/landing light introduced on the Hind E is located on the lower fuselage just ahead of the nose wheels.

(Below) This late production Hind E carries the latest Hind armament configuration first observed during 1985. The two outboard wing pylons carry racks for Spiral (AT-6) missiles instead of their usual load of UB-32 rocket pods, giving the Hind E/F the capability of carrying a total of eight Spiral anti-tank missiles.

A Hungarian Air Force Hind E, Red 711, conducts a fly-by during an air show at Buda-Örs airfield in 1986. The fuselage side number is in Red with a thin White outline. The national insignia is carried on the fuselage sides and on the belly under the main cabin doors.

Mi-24 Hind F

In 1982 the Soviets unveiled yet another variant of the Hind during Exercise Friendship 82. The new variant, assigned the NATO code name Hind F, appeared to be a modified Hind E with the nose turret removed and a GSh-23 23MM twin barrel cannon pack fitted to the starboard side of the nose. The twin barrels of the cannon are fitted with prominent flash arresters to prevent the gunner from being blinded when the weapon is fired. The cannon has a rate of fire of 3,400 rounds per minute and a maximum range of 3,300 feet. The weapon is loaded through two doors on the starboard fuselage below the pilot's cockpit door. Although greatly upgrading the Hind's firepower, the fixed cannon installation has one major tactical disadvantage. Unlike the US AH-64 Apache, which has a cannon mounted in a turret, the Hind F must maneuver the whole aircraft to bring the cannon to bear on a target and consequently cannot engage multiple targets simultaneously with its missiles and gun.

The cannon armament does provide the Hind F with the capability of engaging both ground and air targets at a much greater distances than the earlier 12.7MM machine gun, and with far greater striking power. To date the Hind F is believed to be only in service with the Soviet Air Force, but as more Russian regiments are re-equipped with this variant, the aircraft will probably be exported to members of the Warsaw Pact.

The first Hind Fs in operational units carried neither the chaff/flare dispenser or the infrared counter measures jammer. Later, during 1985, these changes were incorporated on the Hind F and aircraft deployed to East Germany were seen with both the chaff/flare dispenser under the tail boom and the IRCM jammer platform on the engine cover fairing. Additionally the Hind F is fitted with a new type of IFF antenna on the nose and tail.

It is believed that the Hind F has the same modifications as the earlier Hind E and can carry at least eight Spiral (AT-6) missiles. If the missile can be carried on all weapons stations, the Hind F is one of the most heavily armed anti-tank helicopters in the World.

The Hind D, E, and F are expected to remain in service with the Soviet Union and Warsaw Pact well into the 1990s. Production (over 3,000 of all variants to date) will continue both to satisfy export customers and Soviet requirements for the foreseeable future, even though the Hind F's successors, the Mi-28 Havoc and Kamov Hokum, will soon be entering service.

The Hind F was first seen by Western observers during the Warsaw Pact exercise Friendship-82. The doors above the GSh-23 23MM cannon pack are the access doors for the cannon's ammunition bay. The small blister on the low light TV sensor housing is only seen on Hind Es and Fs.

Originally given the interim NATO designation Hind E Modified, these Hinds were equipped with twin barreled GSh-23 cannon packs and have been renamed the Hind F. The turret has been removed and the nose has been modified with a smoothly rounded fairing. The Odd Rods IFF antennas on the nose and tail have been replaced by a new style IFF antenna.

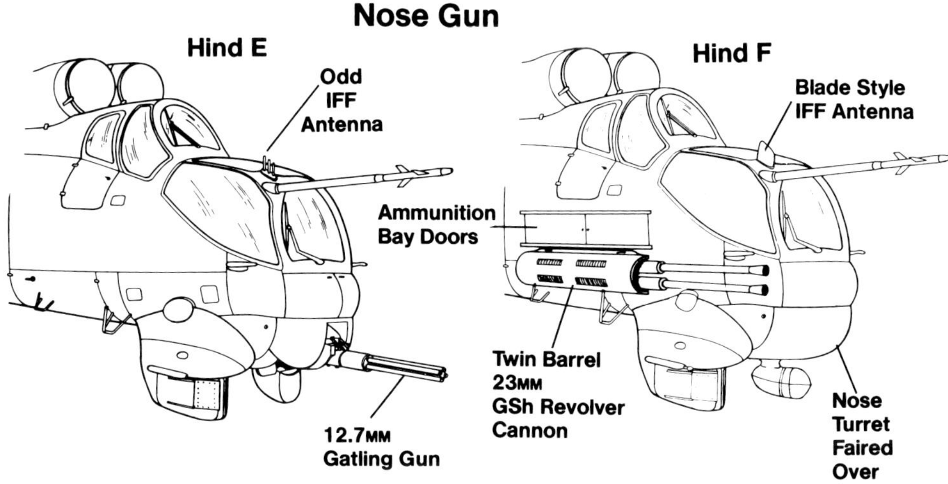

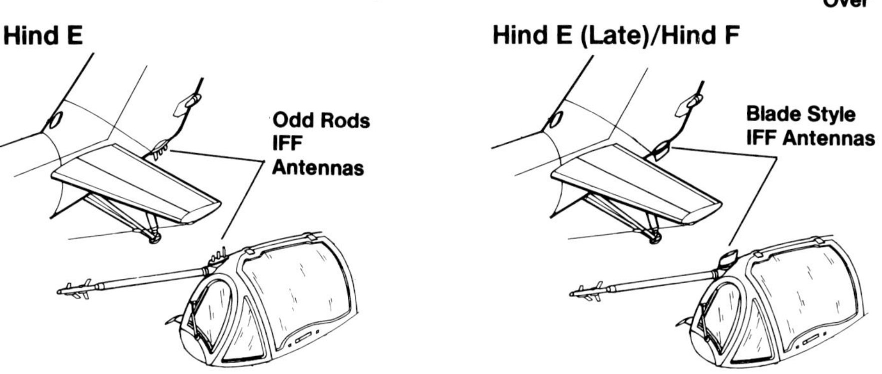

Combat Helicopters
from Squadron/ Signal

1014 Gunslingers in Action
The story of the modern day gunfighter — helicopter gunships in Vietnam. 99 photos, 10 detail drawings, 9 color photos and paintings, 50 pages.
ISBN 0-89747-013-3
Soft Cover **$5.95**

1075 UH-1 Huey in Action
The American Helicopter that revolutionized warfare, becoming synonomous with the Vietnam war, where it was used in a multitude of variants from gunship to ambulance. 100 photos, 50 detail drawings, two pages of scale drawings, 13 full color paintings, 50 pages.
ISBN 0-89747-179-2
Soft Cover **$5.95**

5001 Huey
With thrilling eyewitness accounts of flying and fighting in the Huey, Bell's UH-1 is covered in all its variants, both wartime and peacetime, with over 15 countries being represented. 168 B&W photos, 18 1/72 scale drawings with 2 four-views, 12 color paintings and 36 color photos. 64 pages.
ISBN 0-89747-145-8 **Soft Cover** **$6.95**

6040 Airmobile: The Helicopter War in Vietnam By Jim Mesko
The history, organization, and development of the tactics and weapons of the US Army's helicopter force in Vietnam. From its small inauspicious beginnings as a medical evacuation team in 1961, to its fully evolved form at the end of the conflict when gunships and troopcarriers could darken the sky. Airmobile grew from the 8th and 57th Companies (light helicopters) to the fully deployed 1st Cavalry Division (Airmobile) and 101st (Airmobile) Division. 140 photos, 2 maps, 21 color paintings, 19 color photos, 64 pages.
ISBN 0-89747-159-8 **Soft Cover** **$8.95**

squadron/signal publications, inc.

AD SKYRAIDER in action

by Jim Sullivan
illustrated by Don Greer

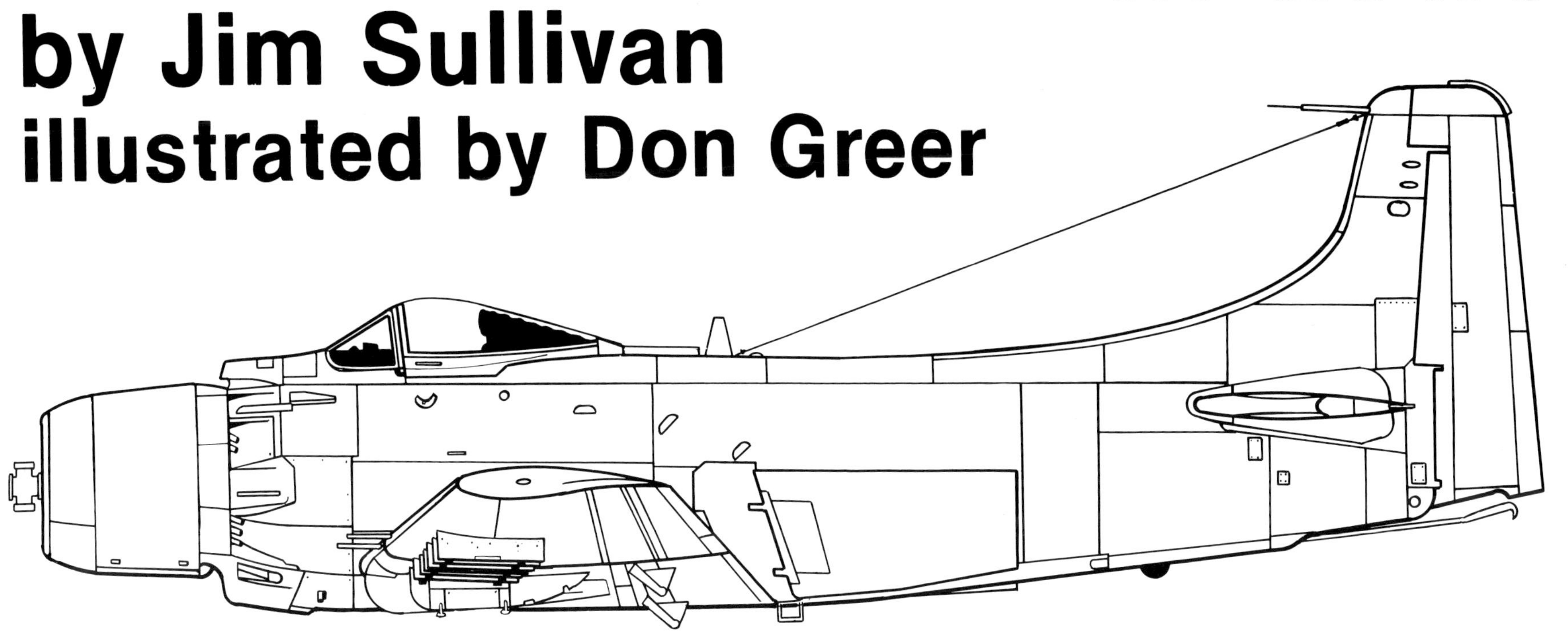

Aircraft Number 60

squadron/signal publications

Lifting off, an AD-4 Skyraider of VF-54, heads for a target in North Korea, carrying a full load of bombs and napalm from the deck of the USS Essex on 3 March 1952. Skyraiders of Air Group Five (VA-55), flying from the USS Valley Forge, participated in the very first Naval Air attacks against North Korean targets on 3 July 1950.

This AD-4 (123827), has been restored to the markings worn during its active duty career. Pilot Dave Forest taxis the NAS Atlanta marked Skyraider during a Valiant Air Command Fly-In at Wilmington, N.C. on 12 April 1981. (Jim Sullivan)

1115 CROWLEY DRIVE, CARROLLTON, TEXAS 75011-5010

ISBN 0-89747-144-X

If you have any photographs of the aircraft, armor, soldiers or ships of any nation, particularly wartime snapshots, why not share them with us and help make Squadron/Signal's books all the more interesting and complete in the future. Any photograph sent to us will be copied and the original returned. The donor will be fully credited for any photos used. Please send them to: Squadron/Signal Publications, Inc., 1115 Crowley Dr., Carrollton, TX 75011-5010.

Dedication:

This book is dedicated to the pilots and ground-support people who handled and maintained this powerful and most effective attack plane, the AD SKYRAIDER.

Acknowledgements

The author would like to thank all the people who have provided material to help make this book possible:

Hal Andrews
Dana Bell
Roger Besecker
Warren Bodie
Peter Bowers
Bill Curry
Tom Curry
Bob Esposito
Don Fetters
W.F. 'Fritz' Gemeinhardt
Richard Hill
Don Jay
Bill Larkins
Peter Mancus
Paul McDaniel
David Moriarty
Walt Ohlrich
Harold Reutebuch
Fred Roos
Doug Slowiak
Flight Leader Russell-Smith
Bob Stuckey
Norm Taylor
Ira Ward
John Woods
The National Archives
USMC History Center
The National Air and Space Museum of the Smithsonian Institution

An AD-4 (123841) of VA-115 banks gently starboard. Belonging to Air Group Eleven, this Skyraider later saw Korean combat from the deck of USS Philippine Sea. 10 June 1950 (National Archives)

V
123841
518

INTRODUCTION

As a replacement for the obsolete SBD Dauntless, Douglas Aircraft Company at El Segundo developed the XSB2D Destroyer, a single engine two place dive bomber with the secondary capability of torpedo attack. Equipped with a tricycle landing gear, and inverted gull wings similiar to the F4U Corsair, the Destroyer was armed with two 50 caliber machine guns mounted in each wing and three 50s mounted in remotely controlled aft turrets. Maximum bomb load was 4000 lbs., which was carried internally.

However, while the two place Destroyer was under development, the Navy changed it's requirements from a two place SB (Scout Divebomber) to a single place BT (Divebomber Torpedo Attack). Douglas quickly went to work redesigning the XSB2D into a single seat aircraft under the designation XBTD-1. Unfortunately the inverted gull wing design proved to be impractical and the XBTD-1 project was cancelled in June of 1944.

The Douglas staff immediately went to work on a new design, after having literally created drawings overnight and gotten approval from the Navy the next day. Under the designation XBT2D-1. Douglas was awarded a contract for 15 experimental machines. However, other manufacturers were already at work on competing designs, and Douglas had to meet the same time schedule as those already at work:

Martin	XBTM	powered by a 3000 hp Pratt & Whitney R-4360 engine.
Curtiss	XBT2C	an updated version of the SB2C Helldiver featuring an aft fuselage radar compartment, the forerunner of the all-weather concept.
Kaiser Fleetwings	XBTK	a small light attack bomber powered by a Pratt & Whitney R-2800 engine.
Boeing	XF8B	powered by a 3000 hp Pratt & Whitney R-4360 turning a six bladed contra rotating propeller. An internal weapons bay could carry two 1600 lb. bombs and external racks could carry an additional pair of 1600 lb. bombs.

Setting an engineering design completion date of January 1945, Douglas immediately began designing a completely new aircraft to the new Navy requirements. To insure that the weight restriction of 16,120 lbs. were met, the design team targeted the design to come in at 15,370 lbs., 750 lbs. under the weight restriction.

The XSB2D Destroyer was designed as a replacement for the SBD Dauntless. A change in Navy requirements caused the cancellation of this two place Scout Divebomber.

Martin XBTM-1 Mauler (85162), the second prototype, is in its natural Aluminum finish while undergoing testing at NATC Patuxent River. 19 July 1947. (via Peter Bowers)

Curtiss XBT2C-1 (50881), the third prototype during flight testing near Columbus, Ohio, 1946. (via Hal Andrews)

Kaiser Fleetwings XBTK-1 (44313), the first prototype after flight testing at NATC Patuxent River, 8 August 1945. (via Peter Bowers)

Boeing XF8B-1 retained the older concept of an internal bomb bay for its bombs and torpedos. Powered by the Wasp Major engine, it could fly at 432 mph. 1944. (via Peter Bowers)

XBT2D-1 (09085), the first prototype Dauntless II in natural Aluminum during Douglas factory flight tests on 13 June 1945. (National Archives)

XBT2D-1 (09100) prototype in glossy Sea Blue with White Modex and numbers. 1949 (via Bob Esposito)

The Douglas "Dauntless II", as the new airplane was now called, was designed around the forthcoming 2500 hp Wright R-3350-24 powerplant. However, the new powerplant was proving more troublesome than expected and it was decided to install the Wright 2,300 hp R-3350-8 engine. Armed with a single 20MM cannon in each wing and three bomb racks, one on each wing and one on the fuselage centerline, the XBT2D-1 flew for the first time on 18 March 1945. Two weeks ahead of schedule.

The XBT2D-1 Dauntless II was delivered to Patuxent River Naval Test Center for evaluation on 7 April 1945. Reports from Naval test pilots were glowing, flight characteristics and performance were rated very good, and wave-off characteristics were excellent. Overall the XBT2D Dauntless II was considered to be the best divebomber ever tested at Patuxent River. One of the Naval requirements that the new divebomber exceeded, and one that impressed the evaluation people, was the XBT2D-1's simplicity of maintenance.

The wings were hydraulically folded, and the wheels, like the F4U Corsair, rotated and folded to the rear. The pilot was protected by armor plating in the cockpit area. Fuel capacity in the single internal fuel tank was 350 gallons, and provision was made for an additional external 150 gallon fuel tank to be mounted on the centerline.

On 5 May 1945, the Navy signed a letter of intent to purchase 598 Dauntless IIs, and while this order was cut to 277 aircraft after VJ Day, the XBT2D's competitors did not fair nearly as well. Only the Martin XBTM Mauler received a production order, which was reduced to 99 machines after VJ Day. The Curtiss XBT2C was kept only as a back-up, in case a problem developed with the Dauntless II; the small Kaiser Fleetwings XBTK was dropped from the competition after flight problems developed; and the Boeing XF8B was cancelled after VJ Day.

The continuation of the Douglas program was largely because of the BT2D's versatility and adaptability. Early in the program aircraft were assigned and modified to become prototypes for a variety of specialized roles:

(P) Photographic

(W) Airborne Early Warning

(N) Night Attack

(Q) Electronic Countermeasure

Of the original 25 XBT2D-1 prototypes built, nineteen were built in the basic Attack Bomber configuration; two airframes (09098/09099) were modified as XBT2D-1N Night Attack; one as a XBT2D-1P (09096) Photo Reconnaissance model; one XBT2D-1Q (09109) all weather machine; one airframe was configured to a XBT2D-1W early warning flying radar station; and the 25th prototype was designated XAD-2. Of the first 25 machines only the first four were powered by the Wright R-3350-8, the balance were powered by the more powerful Wright R-3350-24W.

In February 1946, the BT2D Dauntless II was renamed the Skyraider, and in April when the Navy completely revised it's aircraft role designation system, the BT2D Skyraider became the AD Skyraider.

XBT2D-1Q (09109), the only Electronic Countermeasures (ECM) prototype built, was radar equipped for all-weather flying conditions. The radar operator compartment was located within the fuselage just aft of the cockpit. 1948. (via Hal Andrews)

XBT2D-1 (09094) was modified for a unique experiment. The standard pair of 20MM cannon was replaced by a pair of tubes capable of firing 5 inch rockets. Each wing internally carried six rounds of spin-stabilized rockets for ground attack. This system was tested at NOTS Inyokern, CA., during 1946-47, but was not incorporated into 'fleet' aircraft. 7 June 1948. (via Hal Andrews)

Development

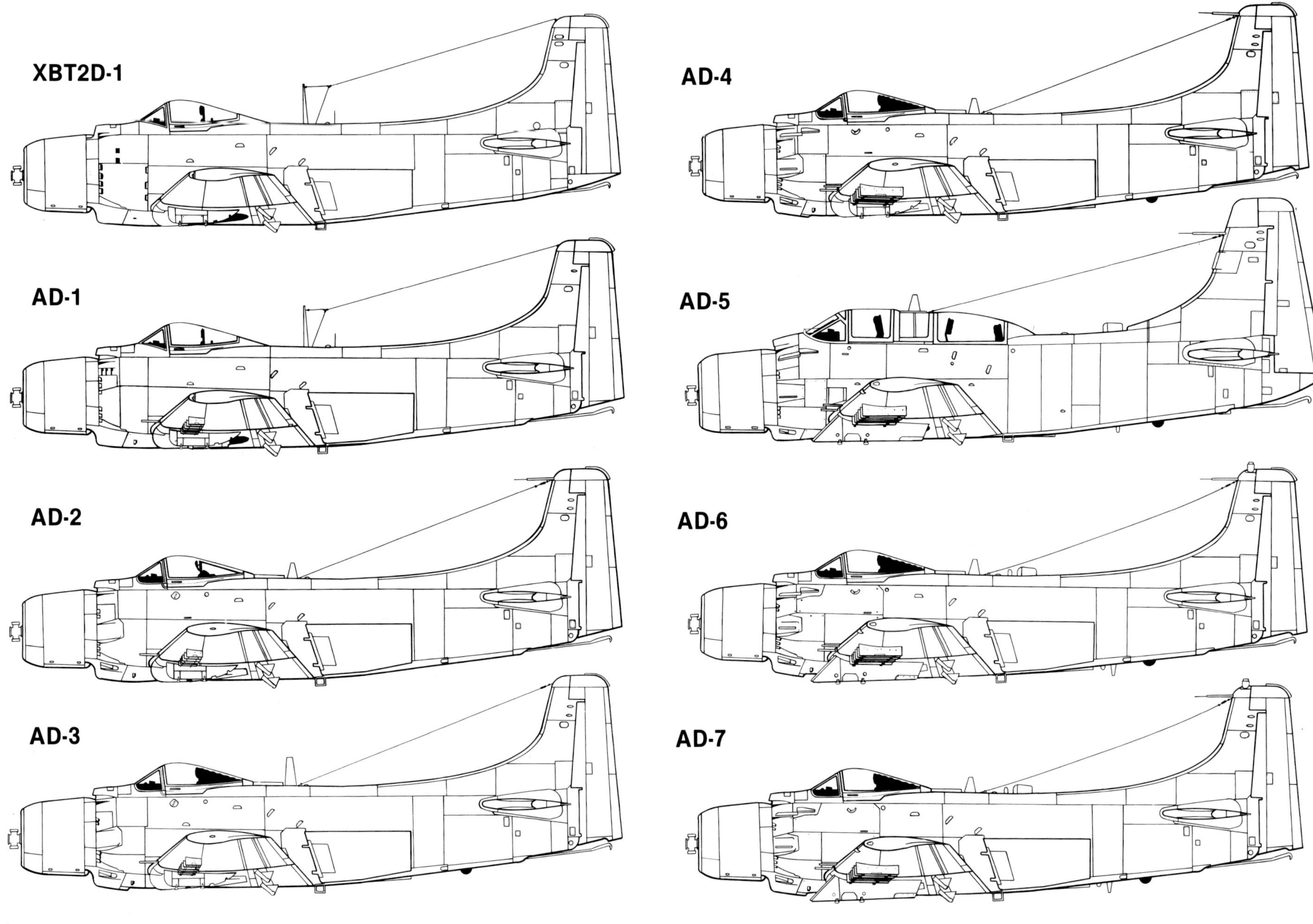

AD-1 Skyraider

AD-1 (09162) from VA-3B during 1948 carrying the markings of USS Franklin D. Roosevelt. VA-3B and VA-4B, attached to CVA-42 on the FDR, were among the first operational squadrons to receive the Skyraider in April of 1947. (via Bob Esposito)

The only changes suggested by the evaluation team at Patuxent River was additional heat and oxygen for the crew, and additional lighting in the cockpit and aft compartment. The AD-1 was at Fleet Air Headquarters, Alameda, California, undergoing service trials, when, during further testing of the XBT2D-1, it was discovered that after repeated carrier landings, structural weaknesses developed that required strengthening in the areas of the landing gear, wing and tail assemblies. These modifications were quickly incorporated into the AD-1 series. Gross weight was 16,500 lbs. and the AD-1 was powered by a R-3350-24W engine turning a 13 ft. 6 in. four bladed prop. This combination produced 2500 hp. Armament was two 20MM cannons (one in each wing), with provisions for six Mark 9 rocket launchers on each outer wing panel, and two bomb racks capable of carrying up to 2000 lbs. each. Maximum speed was 310 knots and range was 1350 nautical miles. By the spring of 1947, US Navy squadrons on the East and West Coasts were receiving the AD-1. The AD-1 series was flown by both the Navy and Marines. By mid-1948, the AD-1 series had completed its production run. From 1947 until mid-1948, Douglas produced two hundred forty-two AD-1 Skyraiders.

Variants

AD-1Q Electronic Countermeasurers (ECM) aircraft. Carried a crew of two and a gross weight of 16,900 lbs., which was the result of the addition of a compartment with-in the fuselage, just aft of the fuel cell, for the radio countermeasures operator and his equipment. Included in the ECM equipment was an AN/APR-1 Search Receiver, an AN/APA-11 Pulse Analyzer, an AN/APA-38 Panoramic Adapter, and a MX-356/A Window Dispenser. Besides the fuselage 'bumps' and antenna, the AD-1Q was easily identified by the ECM compartment windows and doors located on the fuselage sides just aft of the cockpit area. Thirty-five AD Skyraiders were delivered in the AD-1Q ECM configuration.

Carburator Intake

Early XBT2D

AD-1

Cockpit Airducts

AD-1 (09283) of VA-64 launches from the starboard cat off the USS Coral Sea. Markings are White with the tip of the tail in Yellow. 14 September 1948. (National Archives)

AD-1 (09114) of Air Training Unit-301. From this training squadron Naval aviators were assigned to Fleet units. 17 October 1952. (via Hal Andrews)

(Below) AD-1 of VA-6B, has just landed and is folding its wings while taxiing forward aboard USS Coral Sea. The horseshoe marking on the cowling is White. 20 May 1948. (National Archives)

Under Wing Attachment Points

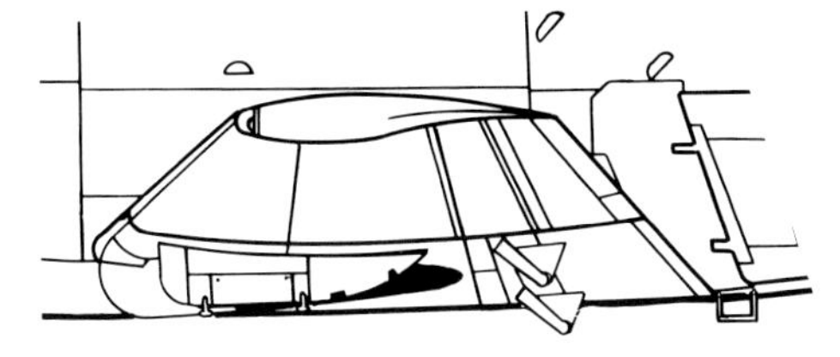

XBT2D-1

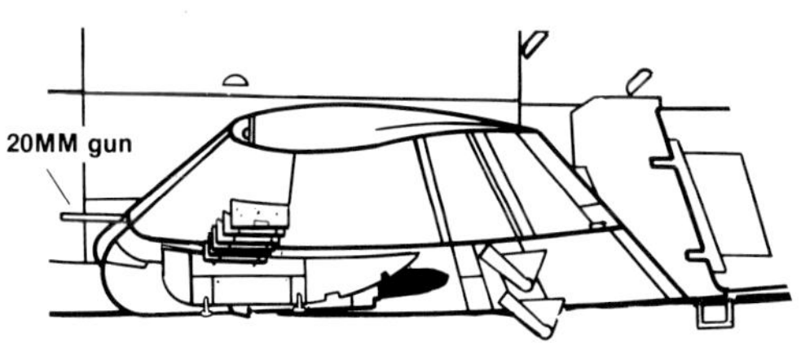

AD-1

AD-1 (09204) of VA-20A based at NAS Alameda, CA, flying along the Pacific coastline near San Francisco. All markings are White on glossy Sea Blue. Note the flat finish forward of the windscreen. The gun muzzle covers are still in place protecting the 20MM cannon. 2 June 1947. (Bill Larkins)

AD-1 (09192) of VA-4B from the USS Franklin D. Roosevelt. The cowl marking is a Green knight on a White shield. The pilot's name, Ens. Bill Newell, is in White forward of the canopy. A standard Mark 12 one hundred-fifty gallon drop tank on the centerline and an AN/APS-4 pod on the wing rack. Wilmington, N.C. 1949 (Paul J. McDaniel)

(Below) AD-1 (09226) of VMAT-20, a Marine training unit based at MCAS El Toro, CA. Note the canvas cover on the wing folding mechanism and a Mark 12 one hundred-fifty gallon drop tank on the wing. 1953. (via Bill Larkins)

AD-1Q (09366) from VX-1, a weapons development squadron carries an AN/APS-4 radar pod under the port wing. The port window of the ECM operator's compartment can be seen between the White 10 and the national insignia. The ECM operator's entry hatch is on the starboard side. 6 January 1949. (National Archives)

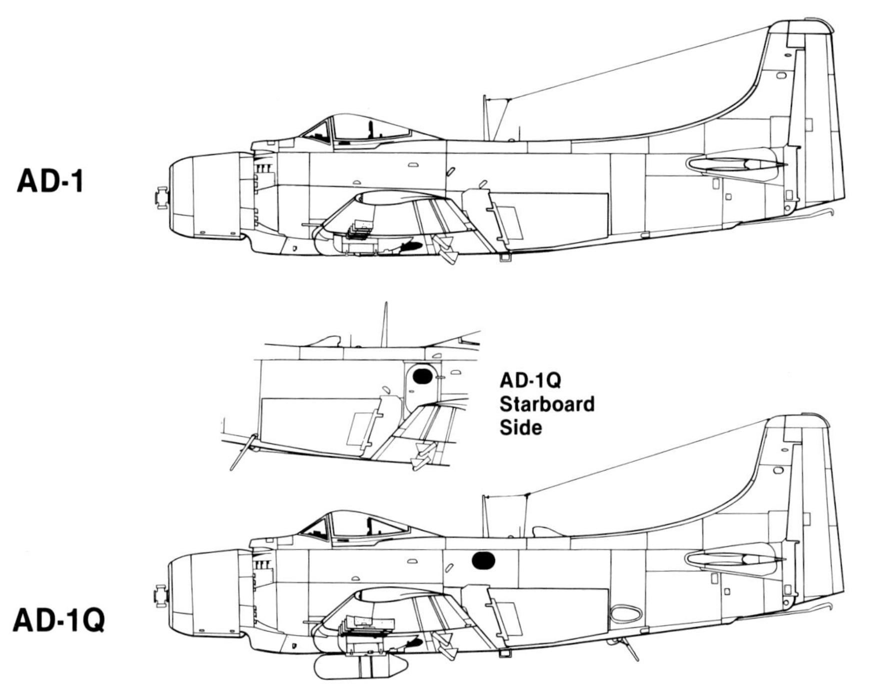

Factory fresh AD-1Q (09354) with an ECM pod beneath each wing. The AD-1Q carried a crew of two. El Segundo, CA. August 1947. (via Hal Andrews)

AD-1Q (09359) of VC-35 with an ECM blister on the lower rear fuselage, and antennae on the bottom of the rear fuselage. Note the airscoop just aft of the radio mast. It was used to cool the ECM equipment. 1949. (via Bill Larkins)

AD-2 Skyraider

Continued structural failure caused by hard carrier landings, despite the beefing up which had already taken place, continued to plague the AD-1. These problems were solved on the AD-2, with AD-1s being rebuilt to the new standards.

The AD-2 was a much revised and improved airplane. The new 3,020 hp R-3350-26W powerplant, capable of lifting a 6,650 lb. payload, was a major improvement. The exhaust collector ring was revised, as were the exiting exhaust pipes. With the addition of an external fuel tank, fuel capacity was increased to 500 gallons in the scouting role. The AD-2 could take off at 80 to 85 knots, would stall at 75 knots, and had a top speed of 328 knots. Range was 1,386 nautical miles.

Numerous cockpit refinements were made, including a revised windscreen and canopy, and the pilots headrest was completely redesigned. Functionally designed controls (the use of a small flap for the flaps, and a small wheel for the wheels, etc.) were added. A new aerial mast and a revised short aerial wire, running directly to the fuselage, was added, and on later production AD-2s, a pitot tube was fitted to the leading edge of the fin. Hinged undercarriage doors were installed for the first time.

Even with all the changes and modifications, the Skyraiders normal gross weight was only 16,332 lbs. One hundred seventy-eight AD-2s were delivered to the Navy.

Variants

AD-2Q Electronic Counter Measure (ECM) aircraft with a compartment similiar to the AD-1Q. Even with the addition of ECM equipment and associated fuselage modifications, the -2Q performed very similiarly to the -2. Top speed was 317 knots at 18,300 ft., cruise speed was 205 mph, service ceiling was 31,500 ft., and range was 850 miles. 21 AD-2Qs were built.

AD-2QU a one of a kind modification in which a -2Q airframe (122373) was modified with provisions for target towing duties.

Exhaust Development

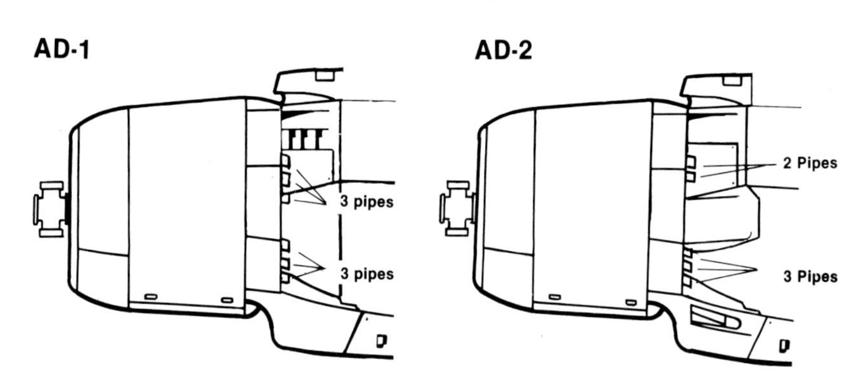

AD-2 (122225), freshly painted in the markings of VA-155, on the ramp at NAS Alameda, CA. This Skyraider was flown by the squadron C.O., LCDR. G.R. Stablein, and carried his name in White below the canopy. A new revised blade aerial mast replaced the older pole styled mast. The new aerial wire ran from the mast to the fuselage. 21 September 1948. (Bill Larkins)

Canopy Development

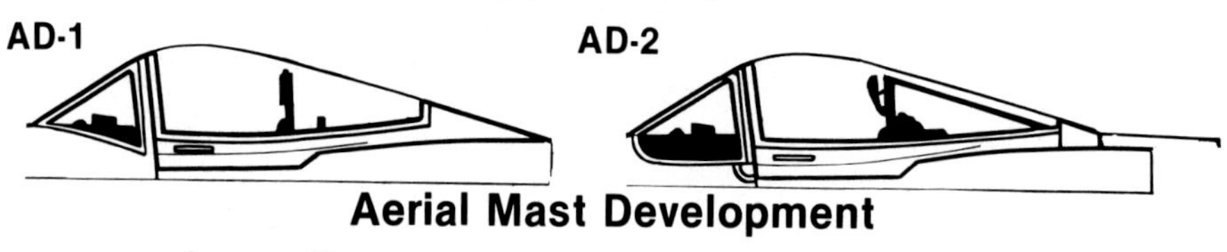

Aerial Mast Development

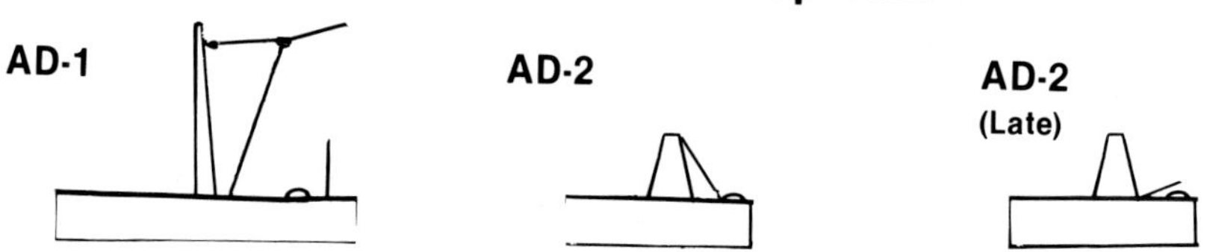

Tail Development

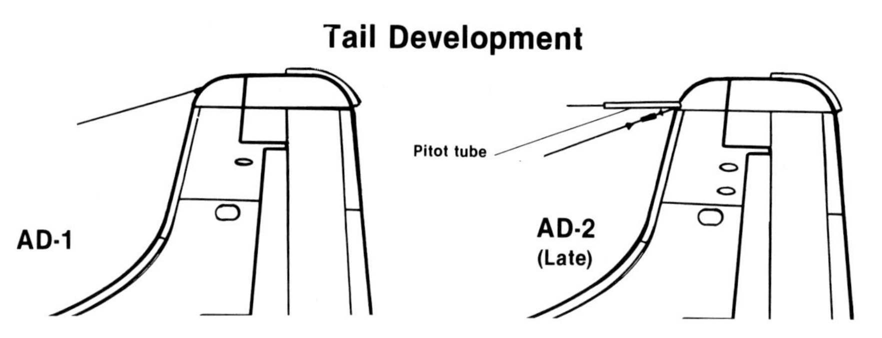

AD-2s of VMA-121 (AK-2 is serialed 122265) fly in echelon during a training flight prior to their Korean combat deployment. The mountainous terrain near MCAS El Toro, CA., proved to be very close to the ground conditions they would encounter in Korea. (Clay Jansson via W.F. Gemeinhardt)

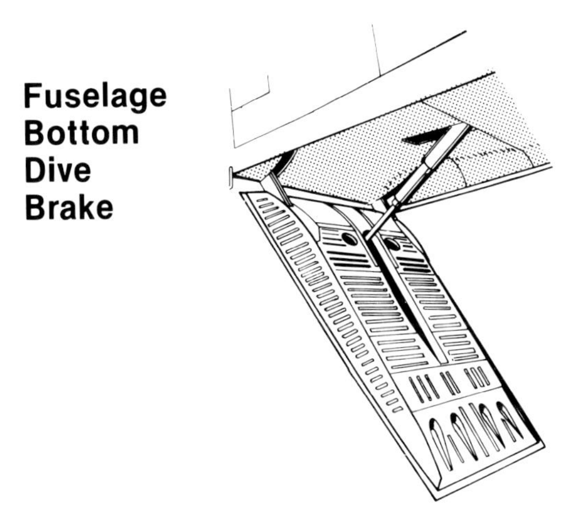

(Below Left) AD-2 (122225) in Korea serving with Marine Aircraft Maintenance Squadron 12 (MAMRON 12) at K-6 Pyongtaek, Korea. 13 November 1953. (Charles Trask via Bill Larkins)

AD-2 (122269) of VA-65 (formerly VA-6B) makes a three-point landing at NAAS Santa Rosa, CA. VA-65 was between combat tours aboard the USS Boxer. August 1951. (Bill Larkins)

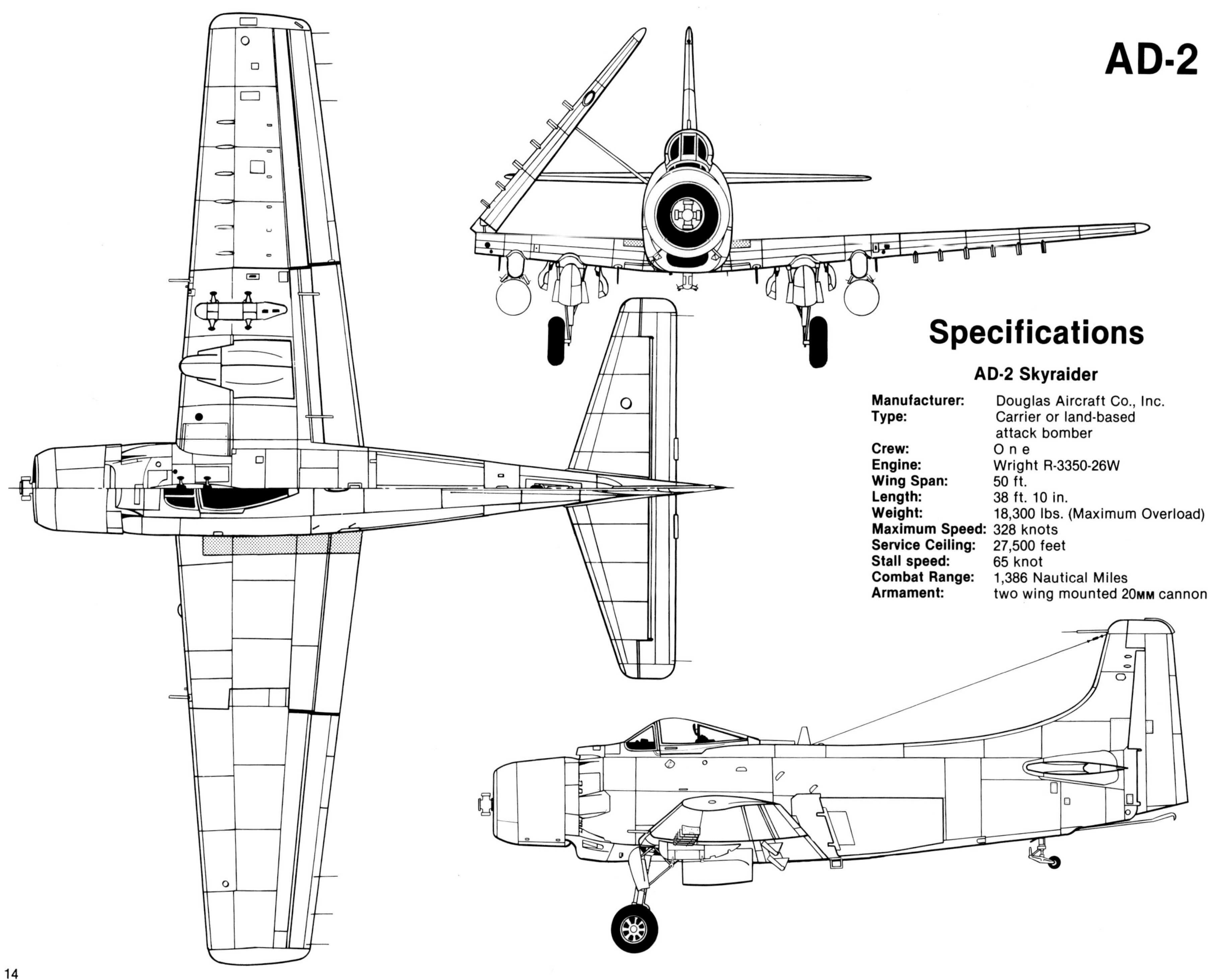

AD-2

Specifications

AD-2 Skyraider

Manufacturer:	Douglas Aircraft Co., Inc.
Type:	Carrier or land-based attack bomber
Crew:	One
Engine:	Wright R-3350-26W
Wing Span:	50 ft.
Length:	38 ft. 10 in.
Weight:	18,300 lbs. (Maximum Overload)
Maximum Speed:	328 knots
Service Ceiling:	27,500 feet
Stall speed:	65 knot
Combat Range:	1,386 Nautical Miles
Armament:	two wing mounted 20MM cannon

CARRIER CRASHES

(Above) AD-2 (122231) of VA-155, goes into a torque roll after taking a wave-off by the LSO aboard the USS Valley Forge. The Skyraider splashed inverted, and the pilot was lost. 31 August 1948. (National Archives)

(Below) AD-2 of VA-35, landed long aboard the USS Leyte off Korea, clipping a 5-inch gun mount with the wing. After trying desperately to fly away, the AD mushed into the ocean. The uninjured pilot was picked up immediately. 10 November 1950. (National Archives)

AD-2 (122251) of VC-33 warms-up prior to take off from NAS Atlantic City, N.J. Note the squadron insignia on the fuselage which can be seen below and in front of the windscreen. 17 July 1951. (via Bill Larkins)

AD-2 (122330), totes a torpedo on the centerline, a pair of 2,000 lb. bombs on the inner wing panels, and twelve 5-inch HVARs on the outer wing panels, during armament testing at the Naval Air Test Center at Patuxent River. (National Archives)

(Below) AD-2 (122234) of VA-859 missed the wires and tangled with the barrier aboard USS Tarawa. The pilot is hastily exiting the burning Skyraider. 7 July 1952. (National Archives)

AD-2 Skyraiders of VA-34 aboard USS Leyte, armed with 3 torpedos and 12 rockets for use during a firepower demonstration. Note how securely the lead AD is tied to the flight deck. May 1949. (National Archives)

Landing gear

Main gear

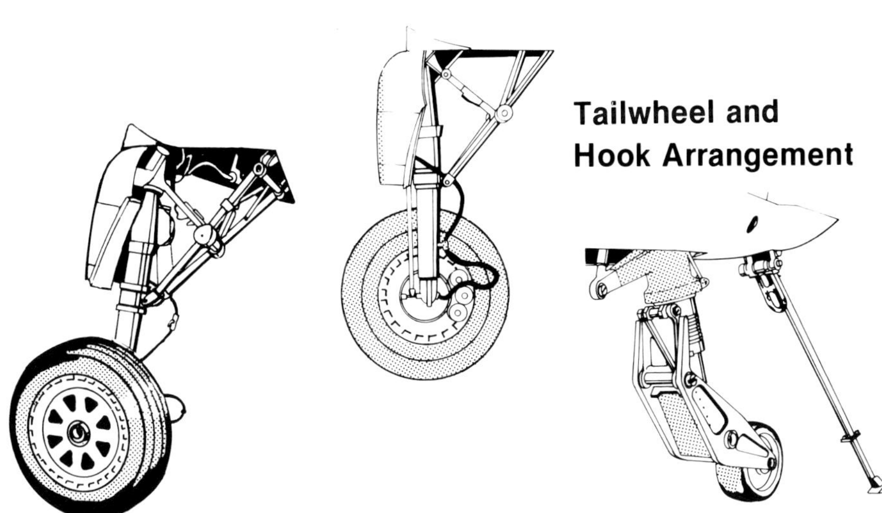

AD-2 (122310) 'Jinx', of VA-702, took AA hits during strikes launched from USS Boxer. It was diverted to a Korean land base for repair. 13 June 1951. (National Archives)

AD-2Q (122366) of VF-152 is seen parked on display at the San Francisco Air Fair. The pilots name, Ens. W.B. Whitten, is painted just forward of the windscreen. Note the AN/APS-4 radar pod on the port wing. 30 October 1949. (Bill Larkins)

AD-2Q (122366), fresh from the production line at El Segundo, CA. It was accepted by the Navy in August of 1948 and served until January of 1952 when it was stricken from inventory. Its last duty was with VC-33. 9 August 1948. (via Hal Andrews)

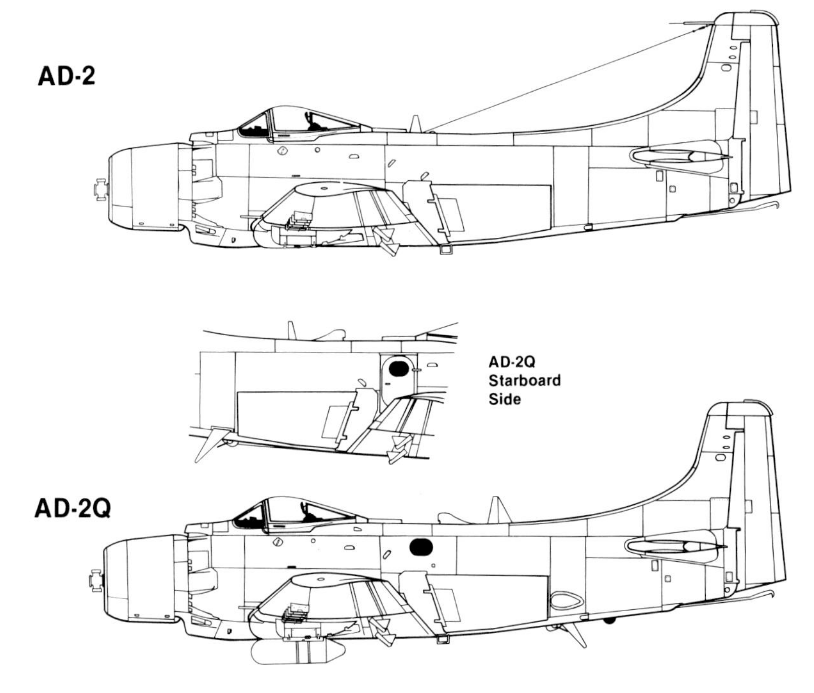

AD-2Q (122383) of VC-33 on the flight line of NAS Norfolk, VA, where the 'Night Hawks' were stationed. Note the dull finish on the cowlings. 1949. (via Peter Mancus)

AD-2 Canopy

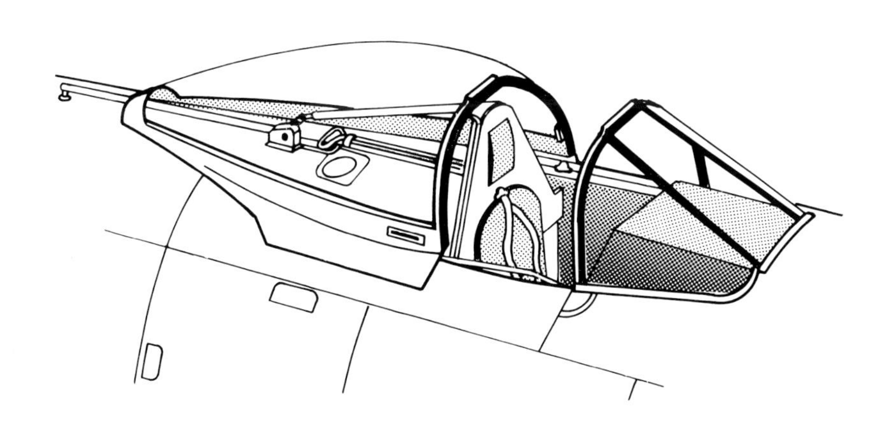

AD-2QU

AD-2QU (122373), a one-of-a-kind conversion for target-towing duty is parked on the ramp at NOTS Inyokern, CA. 1952. (via Bob Esposito)

AD-3 Skyraider

Under the designation AD-3, few changes were made. The main landing gear oleo stroke was lengthened by 14 inches. The tail wheel was revised and was no longer fully retractable, but now protruded slightly below the fuselage during flight. The propeller was improved and the cockpit was further refined. The pitot tube added to the tail of the -2 was deleted and the antenna wire was re-arranged. The bottom of rudder was changed slightly in shape. Top speed was 325 knots at 18,300 feet and range was 1,310 nautical miles. When production terminated in mid-1949, one hundred ninety-four AD-3s had been produced.

Variants

AD-3Q ECM aircraft with a revamped ECM compartment and antenna system. Twenty-two were produced.

AD-3W Airborne Early Warning Aircraft, a three man version with a large belly mounted radome housing search radar. This configuration was nicknamed "Guppy". Thirty-one were produced.

AD-3E Modified from AD-3W aircraft, with special electronic equipment. Two were produced.

AD-3N Night Attack aircraft carrying a crew of three. Fifteen were produced.

AD-3S Anti-submarine Warfare (ASW) aircraft. Two were built from AD-3N aircraft.

AD-3 (122799) of VA-35 just landed on board USS Leyte off the Korean coast. The rudder tip is Green, all other markings, with the exception of the Red bar in the insignia, are White. 12 November 1950. (National Archives)

AD-3 (122732), during testing at NATC Patuxent River, carrying a 2,000 lb. bomb on the centerline and an AN/APS-4 radar pod on the port wing rack. The AD-3 was capable of 325 knots. 8 March 1949. (USN via Hal Andrews)

"Hefty Betty", an AD-3 (122737) from VA-923, ready to launch from USS Bon Homme Richard off the coast of Korea. This unit was called up for duty from NAS St. Louis, MO. Note the addition of a single piece exhaust glare shield just behind the cowling. October 1951. (via John Woods)

AD-3 (122805) of VC-12, gets chewed up by a landing AD-4Q (124042) of VC-33 on board USS Leyte. Both aircraft suffered strike damage, and one of the pilots was killed. 14 January 1952. (USN via Walt Ohlrich)

Ens. Harold Reutebuch of VA-923 in the battle-damaged cockpit of an AD-3 (122760) aboard Bon Homme Richard. Air Group Commander H. Funk points to another AA hit. 8 July 1951. (USN via Harold Reutebuch)

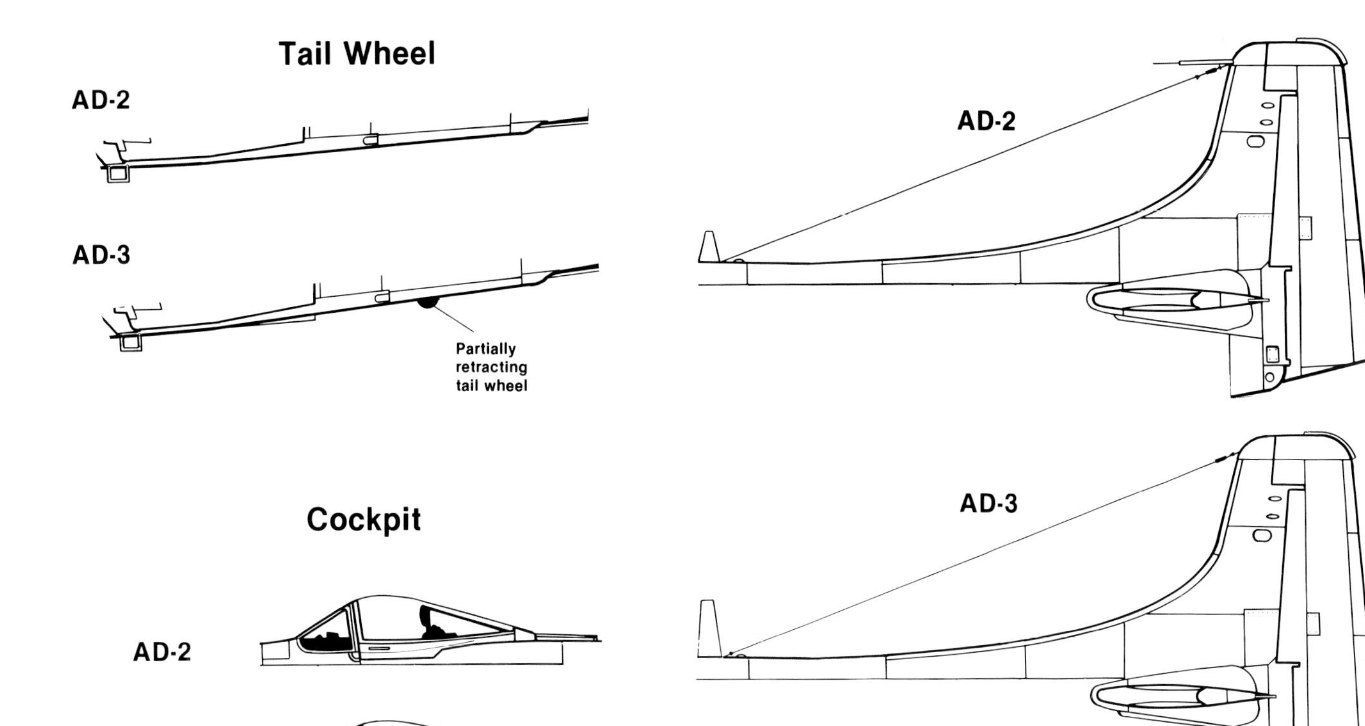

AD-3 (122875) of VC-33 has heavy AA damage to the tail section, sustained while on a mission near the Yalu River. Pilot, Ens. R.H. Rohr, made an emergency landing at Pyongyang, Korea. 24 November 1950. (National Archives)

AD-3Q (122854) is factory fresh as it prepares for its Navy acceptance flight. 854 is carrying the AN/APS-4 radar pod under the port wing. El Segundo, CA. 18 May 1949. (via Hal Andrews)

AD-3Qs (NR 60 is 122866) of VC-35 fly a starboard echelon formation. A detachment of four of these (ECM) aircraft were assigned to each Fleet carrier. 13 March 1951. (National Archives)

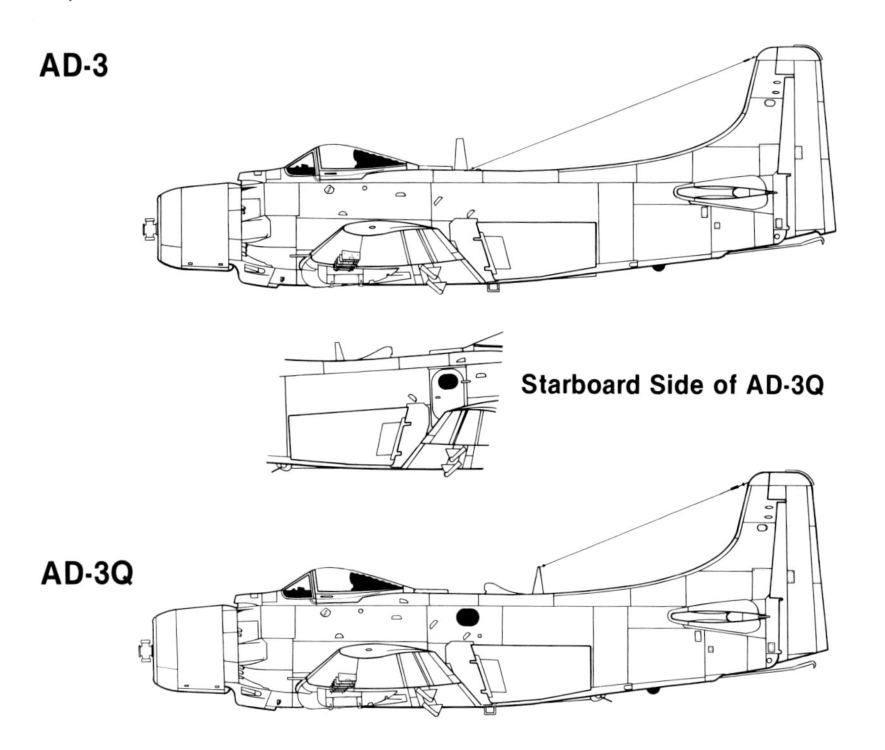

AD-3Q
Cockpit and ECM Operators Compartment

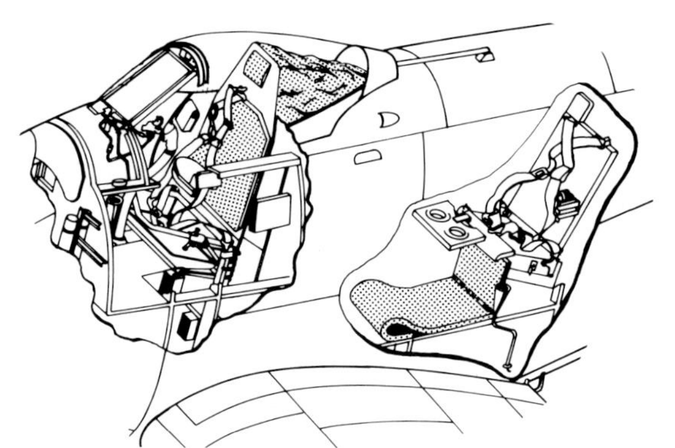

AD-3Ws of VC-11 form the USS Boxer have arrived at an emergency landing field in Korea bringing metalsmiths and parts to repair the damaged wing of another Skyraider. 13 June, 1951. (National Archives)

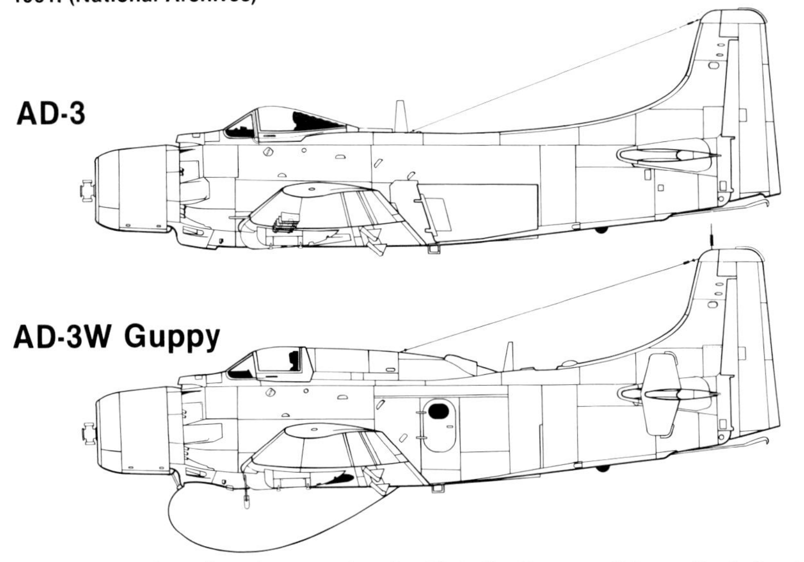

The AD-3W radome housing search radar. Note the Summer flying suits, helmets and life jackets of the crew. Also note the lack of landing gear fairings on this version. NAS Quonset Point, RI. May 1951. (National Archives)

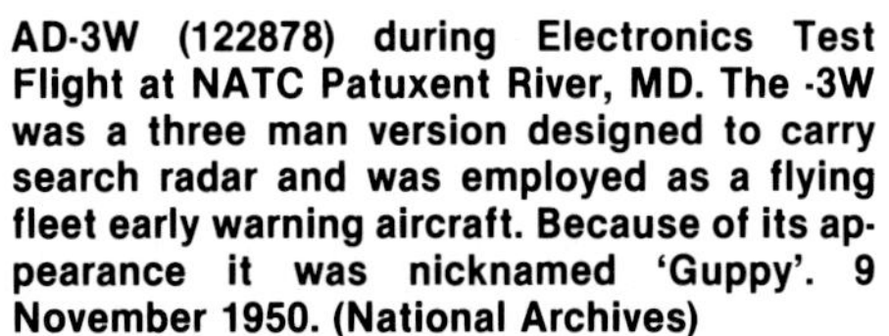

AD-3W (122878) during Electronics Test Flight at NATC Patuxent River, MD. The -3W was a three man version designed to carry search radar and was employed as a flying fleet early warning aircraft. Because of its appearance it was nicknamed 'Guppy'. 9 November 1950. (National Archives)

The second of the two AD-3Es (122907), that were modified from AD-3Ws, uses a booster generator during the extreme cold of the winter aboard USS Valley Forge off Korea. December 1950. (National Archives)

(Left) AD-3W Airborne Early Warning aircrew sit side-by-side in the fuselage ECM compartment crammed with electronics gear. This aircraft is getting a thorough inspection prior to a long flight. 3 May 1951. (National Archives)

(Below) One of the two AD-3Es (122906), assigned to VX-1, a development squadron. It is airborne with an AD-3S, both aircraft were stationed at NAS Boca Chica. 31 January 1950. (National Archives)

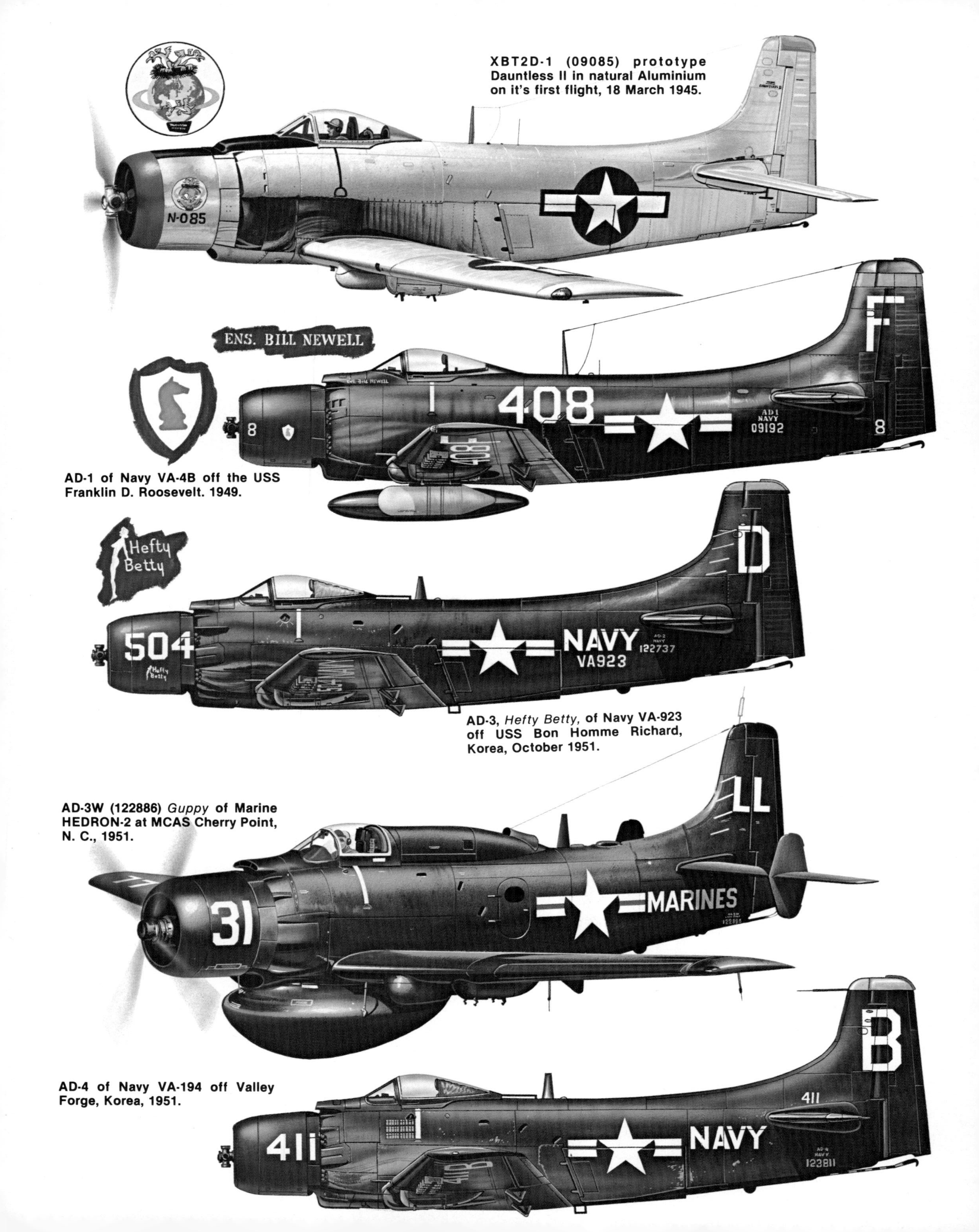

XBT2D-1 (09085) prototype Dauntless II in natural Aluminium on it's first flight, 18 March 1945.

AD-1 of Navy VA-4B off the USS Franklin D. Roosevelt. 1949.

AD-3, *Hefty Betty,* of Navy VA-923 off USS Bon Homme Richard, Korea, October 1951.

AD-3W (122886) *Guppy* of Marine HEDRON-2 at MCAS Cherry Point, N. C., 1951.

AD-4 of Navy VA-194 off Valley Forge, Korea, 1951.

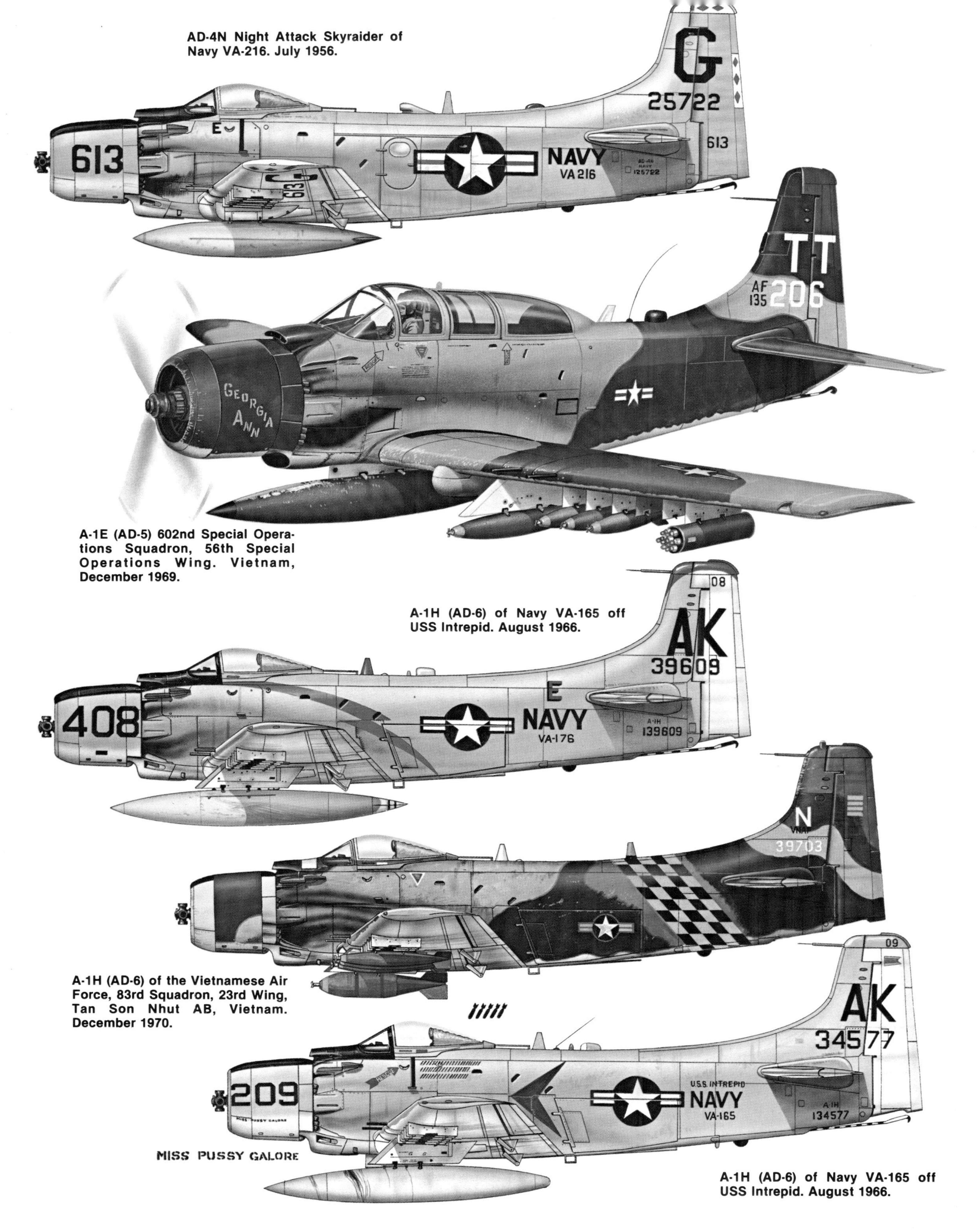

AD-4N Night Attack Skyraider of Navy VA-216. July 1956.

A-1E (AD-5) 602nd Special Operations Squadron, 56th Special Operations Wing. Vietnam, December 1969.

A-1H (AD-6) of Navy VA-165 off USS Intrepid. August 1966.

A-1H (AD-6) of the Vietnamese Air Force, 83rd Squadron, 23rd Wing, Tan Son Nhut AB, Vietnam. December 1970.

A-1H (AD-6) of Navy VA-165 off USS Intrepid. August 1966.

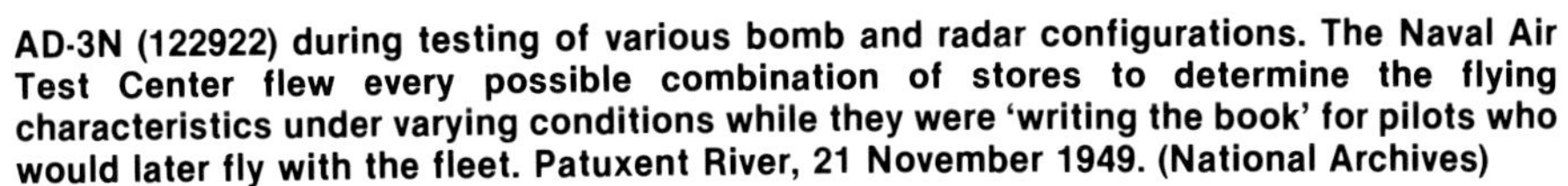

AD-3N (122922) during testing of various bomb and radar configurations. The Naval Air Test Center flew every possible combination of stores to determine the flying characteristics under varying conditions while they were 'writing the book' for pilots who would later fly with the fleet. Patuxent River, 21 November 1949. (National Archives)

(Above Right) AD-3N (122914), marked with three White bands across the top of each wing, is an Electronics Test aircraft. Only fifteen of these -3N Night Attack aircraft were built. NATC Patuxent River. 15 March 1951. (National Archives)

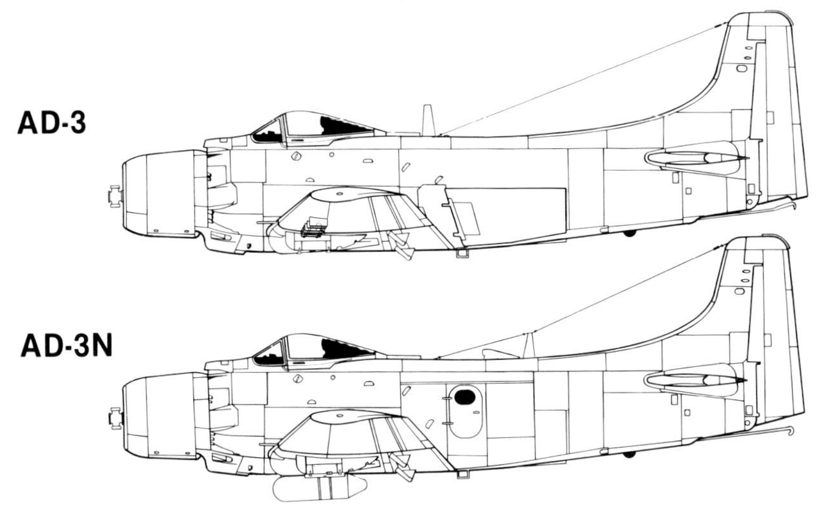

(Middle Right) AD-3S (122910), one of only two machines to be modified from AD-3N nightfighter airframes to the Anti-Submarine Warfare (ASW) configuration. It carries the markings of VX-1 and is flying just off the Florida coast in the Key West area. 31 January 1950. (National Archives)

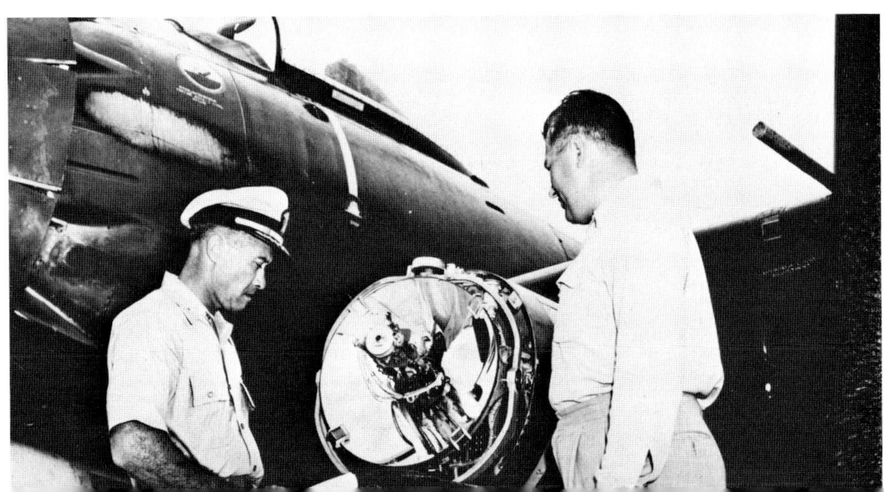

(Right) The other -3S aircraft which was modified to the ASW role, is seen during a routine check of the powerful searchlight assembly used during anti-submarine duty. NAS Boca Chica, FL. 13 June 1951. (National Archives)

AD-4 of VA-728, a Reserve Squadron belonging to Air Group 15, launches from USS Antietam off the Korean coast, intent on inflicting maximum damage on railroad facilities. 25 February 1953. (National Archives)

AD-4 Skyraider

AD-4 (129003) of H&MS-14 with the pilot strapping in for take-off. Philadelphia, PA. 1957. (via Bob Esposito)

The AD-4 featured the installation of the new APS/19A radar that required the installation of a new instrument panel, which included a Mod 3 or Mod 4 bomb directer. A P-1 auto pilot was also installed. The windscreen was redesigned to provide for a wider bullet proof glass in the windshield, and a pitot tube was again fitted to the top of the vertical fin. The powerplant was a Wright 3020 hp R-3350-25WA engine, providing a top speed of 315 knots with a range of 1,110 nautical miles. From the 210th production machine, the AD-4 was armed with an additional 20MM cannon in each outer wing panel. Eventually most AD-4s were retrofitted with the additional 20MM cannons. Outbreak of the Korean War brought about increased production of the AD-4 Skyraider, with 1,051 being produced.

Variants

AD-4L Winterized with de-icer boots on the leading edge of the wings, horizontal stabilizers, and fin. Sixty-three were modified.

AD-4B Nuclear Bomber, with a special Aero 3A center line ejector rack capable of carrying atomic weapons. One hundred sixty-five were produced, which provided the Navy with it's first large scale nuclear capability.

AD-4Q ECM aircraft. Thirty-nine were produced.

AD-4N Night Attack aircraft. Three hundred seven were produced.

AD-4NL Winterized Night Attack aircraft. -4Ns with de-icer boots.

AD-4NA Day attack aircraft. AD-4N Night Attack Aircraft modified to the day attack role.

AD-4W Airborne Early Warning aircraft. Sixty-eight were produced.

Under the Mutual Defense Assistance Program (MDAP) fifty AD-4Ws were provided to Great Britain under the designation AEW.1. From this batch, fourteen AEW.1s went to Sweden for modification as target towing aircraft. France purchased 100 AD-4 and AD-4N Skyraiders. After the Algerian war, the United States tried to re-purchase them for use in Vietnam, France gave many of their remaining Skyraiders to Camobdia instead.

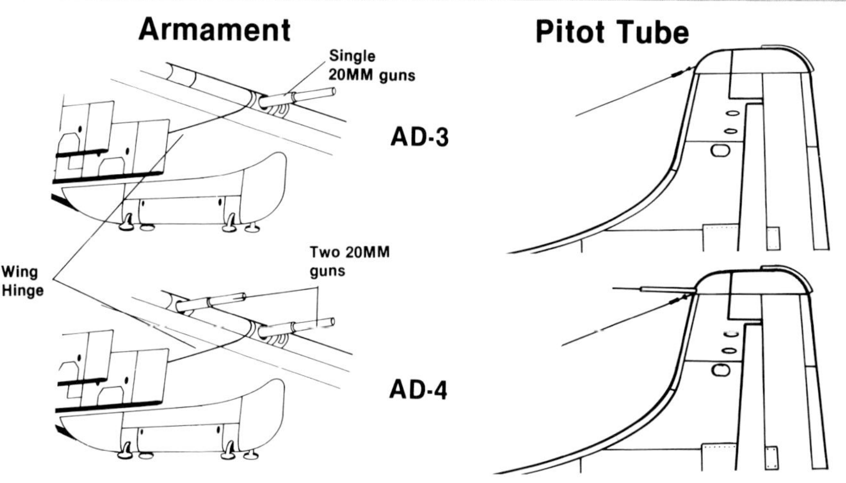

AD-4 Details

Clockwise starting at left top:

(Above Left) View of the cockpit of AD-4 (123816). (National Archives)

(Above) Main panel and portion of right console. (National Archives)

(Above Right) The Visual display from the gunsight. (National Archives)

(Right) The Wright 3,020 hp R-3350-26WA engine. (Dave Forest)

(Below Right) Engine mount assembly. (Dave Forest)

(Below) Bomb-laden AD-4 from VA-115. (National Archives)

(Below Left) RAM rocket armed Skyraider from VA-195. (National Archives)

(Left Center) Engine maintenance. (National Archives)

This AD-4 (123934) of VA-75 was launched from USS Bon Homme Richard, and was damaged by AA fire during a raid over Korea. The Skyraider diverted to a field near Wonsan where it made a safe emergency landing. Determined to be repairable, the AD-4 was towed to Wonsan harbor where it was loaded aboard a barge and taken out to the USS Iowa. It was hoisted aboard the battlewagon and eventually returned to its carrier. September 1952. (National Archives)

AD-4L (123968) of VA-728 crashed aboard USS Antietam. Shortly after this photo was taken, the Skyraider was pushed over the side. 10 July 1951. (National Archives)

AD-4L (127852) with a load of six 5 inch rockets on each wing, an 11.75 inch "Tiny Tim" rocket under the port wing and an ECM pod under the other...this freshly-modified Skyraider was a 'winterized' version with de-icer boots on the leading edges of the wings, horizontal stabilizers and fin. A total of sixty-three AD-4s were modified to 'winterized' AD-4L standards. 1951. (via Bill Larkins)

AD-4L
De-icer Boots

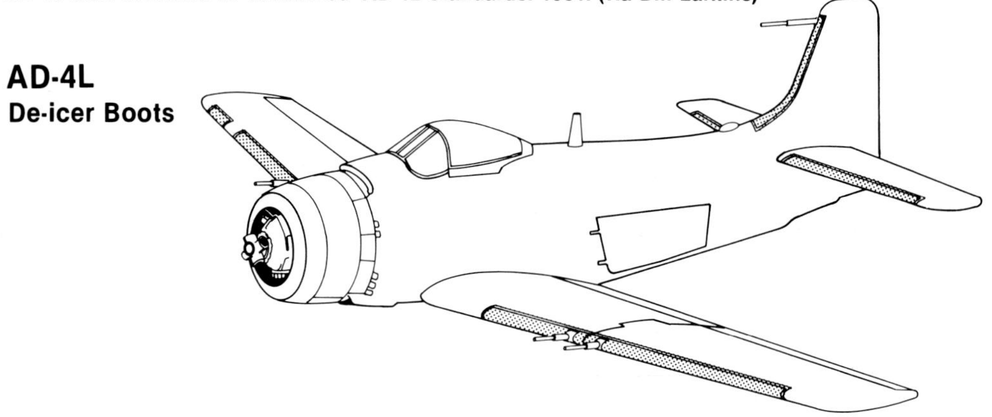

AD-4L (123981) seen after modification at the Douglas factory at El Segundo, CA. 8 March 1951. (via Hal Andrews)

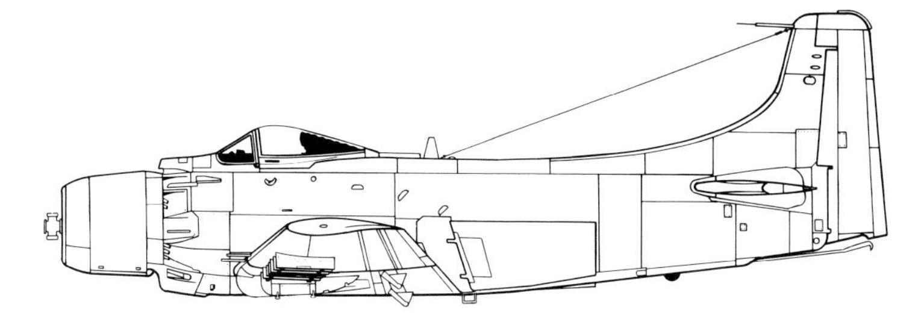

AD-4Q (124056) of CVG-17 off USS Franklin D. Roosevelt. The pilot, Cdr. W.N. Leonard made an emergency landing after the engine main seal blew. The oil covered front of the cowling is a graphic reminder of how close the race was to get the AD on the ground before the engine seized up. 1949. (Paul J. McDaniel)

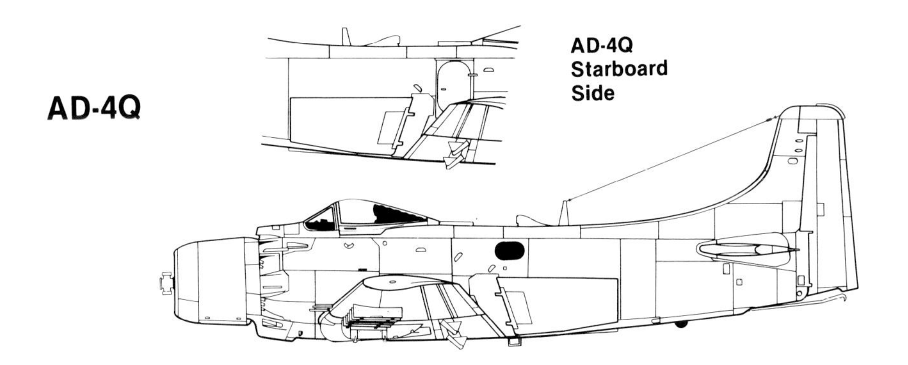

(Right) AD-4Q (124055) of VF-194 lost power on take-off from the USS Boxer and ditched off the port bow. The pilot was quickly recovered unharmed. July 1953. (National Archives)

(Below) Cdr. Funk, the Commanding Officer of CAG-102 just prior to launching in his AD-4Q. Cdr. Funk led the first strike on Korean targets from USS Bon Homme Richard. This machine has not yet been retro-fitted with the additional 20MM wing cannon. 1951. (John Woods via Fred Roos)

AD-4

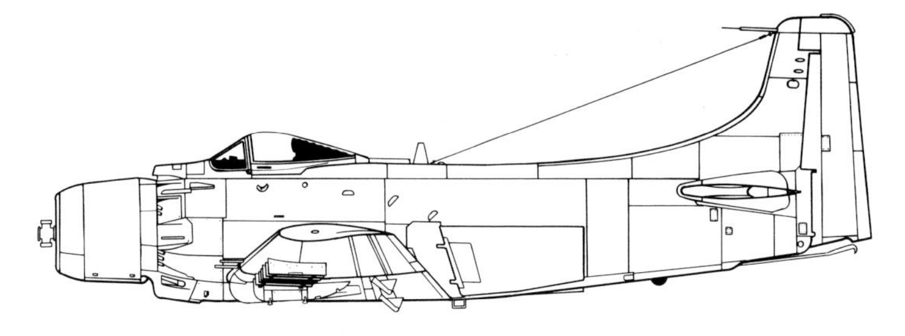

AD-4N (125729) of VMC-3 totes large ECM pod beneath the starboard wing. This version had a three-man crew consisting of pilot, radar operator and ECM operator. MCAS El Toro, CA. 20 February 1953. (National Archives)

AD-4N

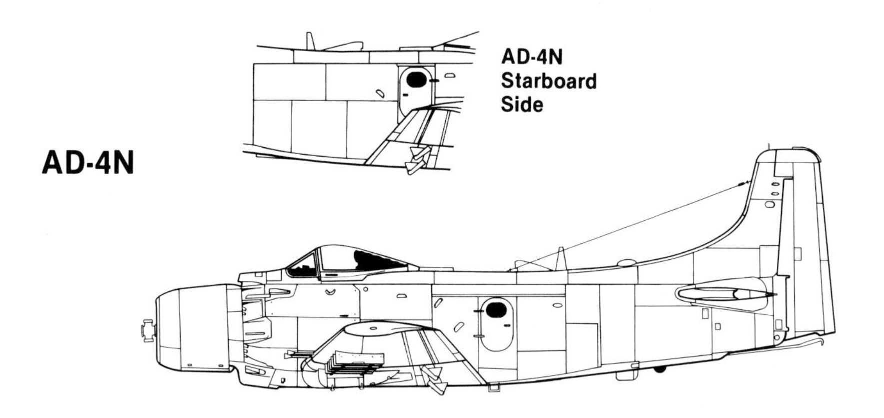

(Right) AD-4N (127014) of VX-3 during a training flight. 1953. (via Paul J. McDaniel)

(Below) "Janet", an AD-4N (125723) of VMC-1, at K-16, Korea, has a slight Blue overspray on all markings including the national insignia. The name "Janet" appears just under the nose number. Note also the replacement ECM compartment hatch with the partial Red and White bar markings. 17 February 1954. (Charles Trask via Bill Larkins)

AD-4N (127011) of Fleet Air Wing Training Unit-Pacific (FAWTUPAC). Note the heavy exhaust pattern on the fuselage. 19 November 1953. (National Archives)

AD-4NA (127011), a night attack AD-4N converted to the day attack role, belonging to FASRON-10, is seen in the change-over paint scheme of Gray and White. On display at NAS Moffett Field, CA. 19 May 1956. (Bill Larkins)

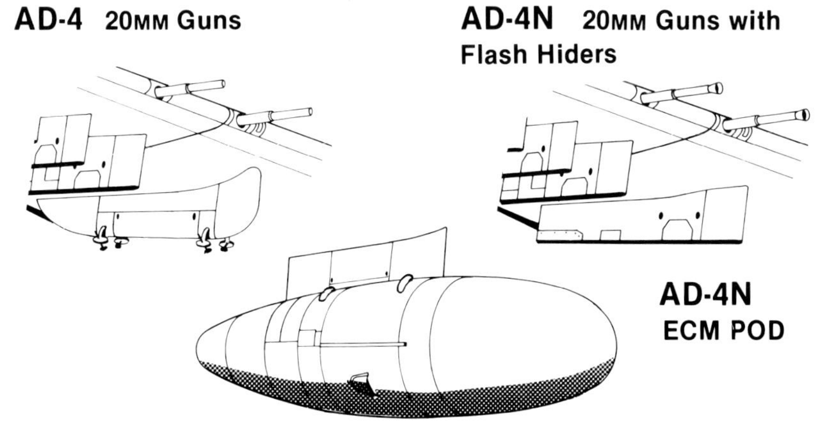

AD-4NL (124741) of VC-35 banks starboard. The 'NL' was modified from the AD-4N as a winterized Night Attack aircraft with de-icer boots. Note the flash shields on the 20MM guns. 6 October 1951. (National Archives)

AD-4B (127871) of HEDRON AFMFPAC is armed with four 20MM cannon in the wings with 200 rounds per gun. The AD-4B had the capability of carrying atomic stores. 1952 (via W.F. Gemeinhardt)

AD-4W (127879) during flight testing at the Naval Air Test Center at Patuxent River. This three place Skyraider was equipped with special electronics gear for the Airborne Early Warning Role. 1950. (via Peter Mancus)

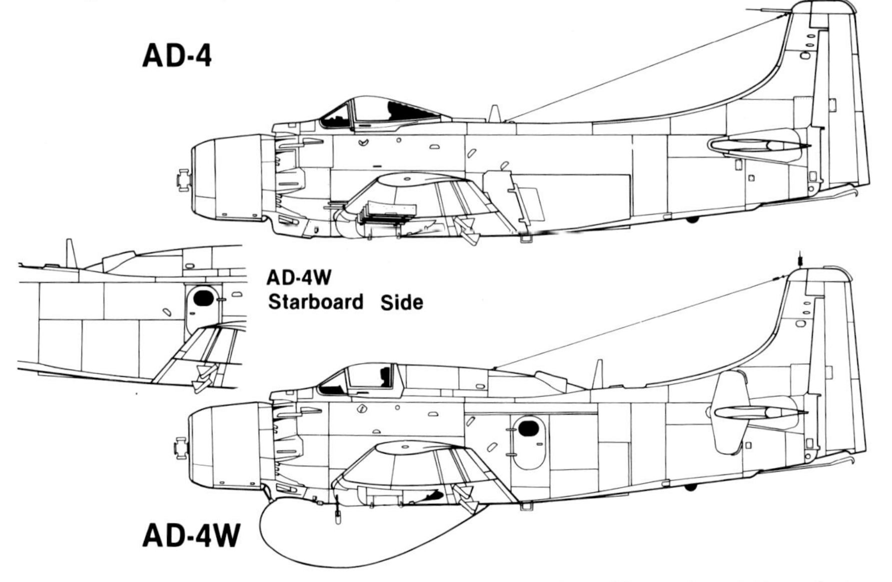

AD-4W (126840) of VMC-1. This aircraft was credited with a 'kill' near Seoul, Korea in June of 1953. (USMC)

AD-4W (124771) of VC-12 on display at the Cleveland, Ohio National Air Races in 1951. This Skyraider was later made available to the English and was modified to an AEW-1 designation, and served with the British Fleet Air Arms as WT-967. (via Bill Larkins)

AD-5 (133926) of VMA-332 "Polka Dots" is fully loaded with twelve HVARs, two 11.75 Tiny Tim rockets and a 500 lb. bomb. 1955. (via Bob Esposito)

AD-5 (A-1E) Skyraider

In the most radical revision of the "Able Dog", the AD-5 was turned into a two place attack bomber with the cockpit crew sitting side by side. To accomplish this increase in cockpit area, the fuselage was lengthened by 23 inches and a completely new canopy and windscreen were designed. To compensate for the change in center of gravity, the uprated 2700 hp R-3350-26W engine was moved forward 8 inches. The vertical tail surfaces were increased by nearly 50% and an airscoop was added to the leading edge of the fin. The antenna system was again revised and the side fuselage dive brakes were deleted. The wing pylons were enlarged and raked forward, and provisions were made for the addition of a centerline pylon, provisions were also made for carrying up to three external fuel tanks. Armament was two 20MM guns in each wing.

First flying 17 August, 1951, top speed was 270 knots with a service ceiling of 26,000 feet and a combat range of 1044 nautical miles. Six hundred sixty-eight AD-5 series were produced with the last aircraft being completed in April 1956.

In the early 1960s, a number of AD-5s were acquired by the USAF's Tactical Air Command for counter insurgency work and saw duty in Vietnam. In the mid-sixties, a number of AD-5 versions were made available to the Vietnamese Air Force.

Variants

AD-5N Night Attack aircraft. One hundred thirty-eight were produced.

AD-5Q Electronic Counter Measures aircraft. Fifty-four machines were converted from AD-5N aircraft for ECM work. The -5Q was the most versatile version of the Skyraider and carried the most complicated electronics ever put together at the Douglas plant. By using a kit concept, the -5 was capable of duties that even included that of ambulance and troop carrier. It became known as the "12 in 1" raider.

AD-5W Airborne Early Warning aircraft. Two hundred-seventeen were produced.

AD-5S Anti-Submarine Warfare (ASW), aircraft. One prototype was produced.

During 1962 the Navy again revised it's aircraft code designation system. The AD Skyraider became the A-1 Skyraider under the following designations.

AD-5	—	A-1E
AD-5W	—	EA-1E
AD-5Q	—	EA-1F
AD-5N	—	A-1G

Canopy Development

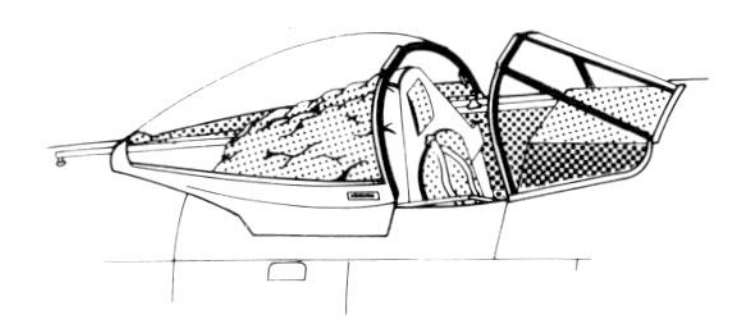

AD-4

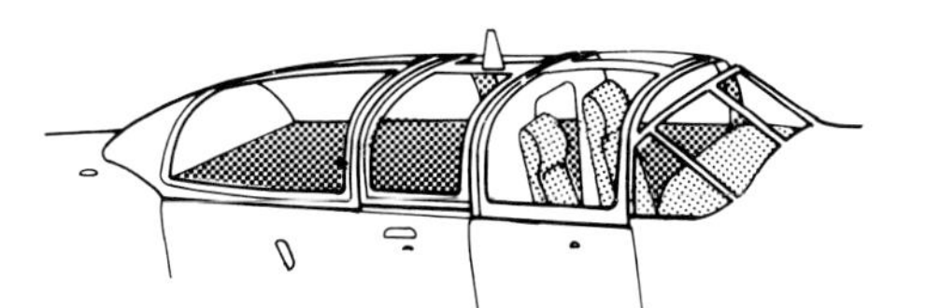

AD-5

(Above) AD-5 (133929) of VA-65 from NAS Alameda, CA., is seen at NRAB Minneapolis, MN. 1956. Tail striping is alternating Medium Green and White. (Bob Stuckey)

(Left) A-1E (AD-5) (133884), with full flaps down (40 degrees), lands at Shaw AFB, SC. 30 March 1968. (Jim Sullivan)

(Right) A-1E (AD-5) (132435) of VA-125 was participating in a search mission when it developed engine problems. The pilot elected to belly-in on a snow covered glacier in the California High Sierras. The pilot was rescued by helicopter, but the aircraft was abandoned. Later the USN turned over ownership to the USAF who took the A-1E out by chopper, refurbished it, and later used it in Vietnam. February, 1969.(USN via Walt Ohlrich)

Pylon Development

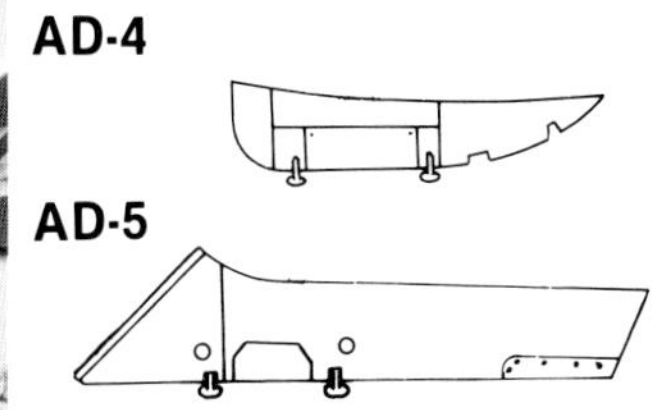

AD-4

AD-5

Air Scoop

Air Scoop

Addition of Air Scoop

(Left) A-1E (AD-5) (132612) of 1st SOS, 14th SOW at Nha Trang AB, RVN. 1965. (R. Leavitt via Doug Slowiak)

AD-5 (A-1E)

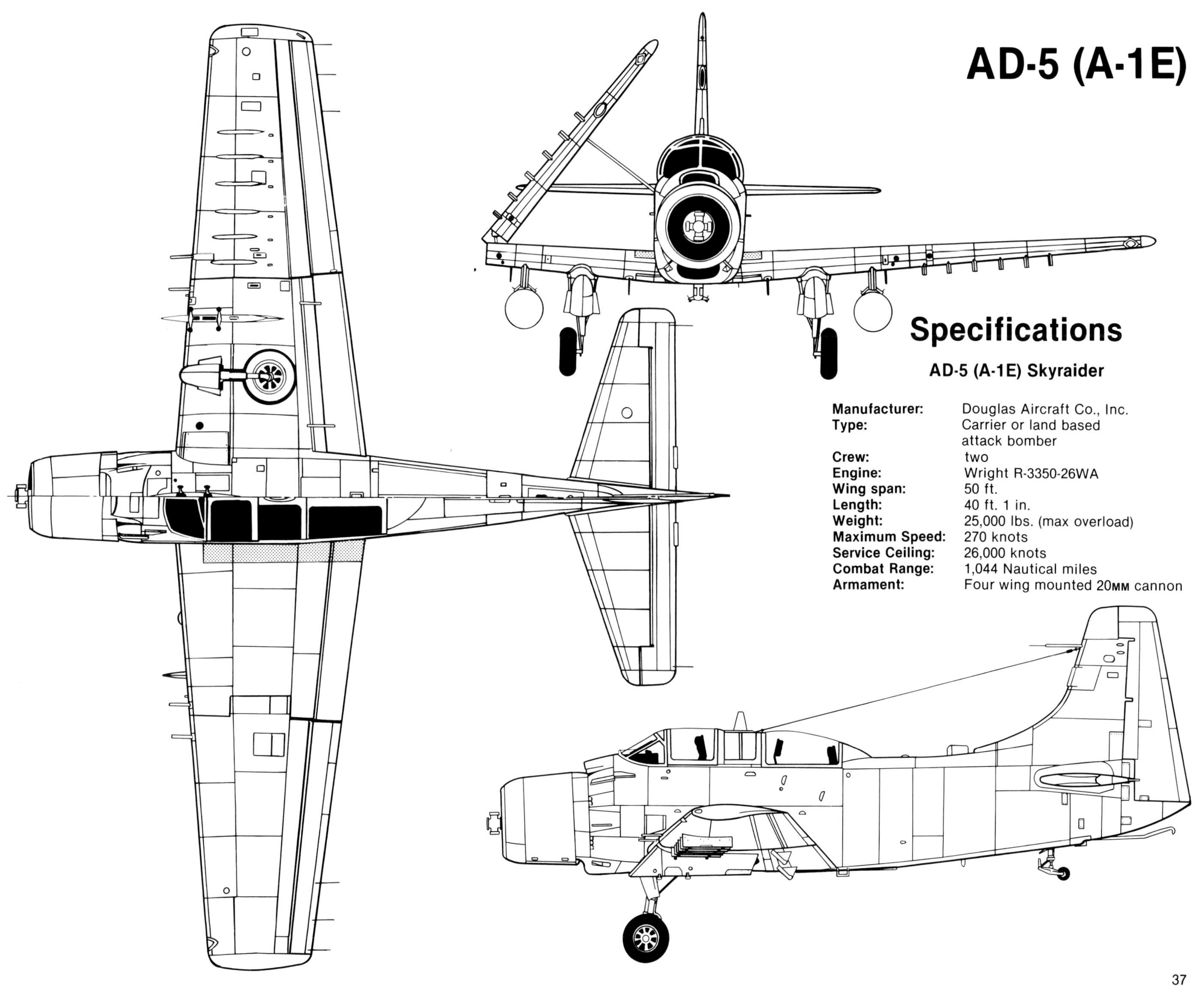

Specifications

AD-5 (A-1E) Skyraider

Manufacturer:	Douglas Aircraft Co., Inc.
Type:	Carrier or land based attack bomber
Crew:	two
Engine:	Wright R-3350-26WA
Wing span:	50 ft.
Length:	40 ft. 1 in.
Weight:	25,000 lbs. (max overload)
Maximum Speed:	270 knots
Service Ceiling:	26,000 knots
Combat Range:	1,044 Nautical miles
Armament:	Four wing mounted 20MM cannon

AD-5N (132553) of VC-33 "Night Hawks". SS Modex on tail and name of squadron on the cowling are in White. The rear cockpit glass is heavily tinted in Blue to screen the sensitive electronic equipment from the sun's rays. 1952. (via Peter Bowers)

(Right) AD-5N (132652) during Douglas flight test. ECM and Searchlight pods are carried on this Skyraider. 1953. (via Hal Andrews)

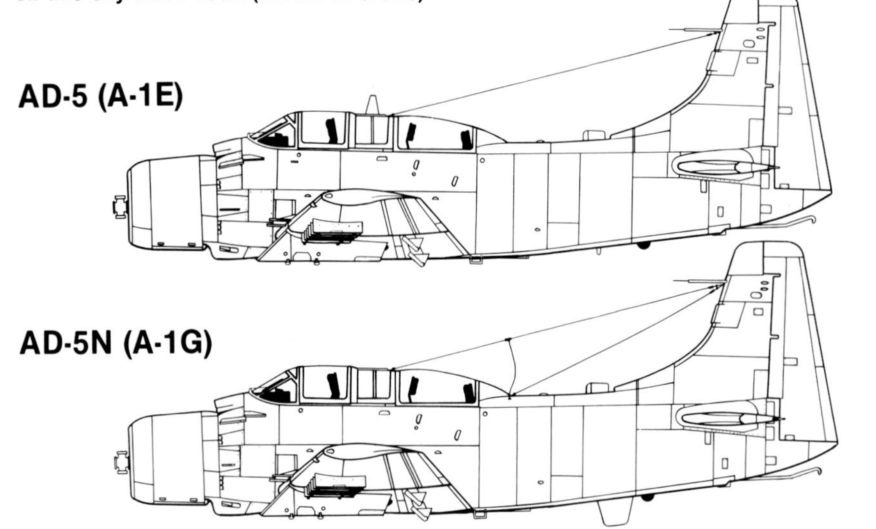

AD-5Ns of VMCJ-3 fly in formation near MCAS El Toro, CA. 1958. (USMC via W.F. Gemeinhardt)

AD-5N (135043) of VAAW-33 during a routine flight. A total of 238 of this night attack version were built. 1960. (via Tom Curry)

A-1G (AD-5N) (134990) in freshly-painted USAF scheme. The Air Force version carries a full complement of under wing racks while the Navy version usually did not. 1966. (via Peter Mancus)

A-1G (AD-5) (135018) of VAW-33 from USS America during stop-over at RAF Luga, Malta. 21 March 1967. (Flight Leader Russell-Smith)

A-1G (AD-5N) (132618) of VAW-33 is flying from USS Independence. This Skyraider could carry a crew of four. 1 May 1962. (USN via Peter Mancus)

EA-1F (AD-5Q) (134994) of VAW-10 is tied down on the flightline at NAS Quonset Point, RI. A major AD re-work facility was located at this Naval Air Station. 17 August 1968. (Ira Ward)

AD-5Q (132506) loaded with Magnetic Anomaly Detection (MAD) gear, ECM pods and radome. Elongated fin and rudder, and fin air intake show to good advantage here. Note test boom installed on starboard wing. July 1957. (via Hal Andrews)

AD-5W (135212) seen landing during SEATO exercise 'Sea Lion' in the South China Sea. Despite the bulky radome, the AD-5W handled little differently than other Skyraiders. 5 April 1960. (USN via Hal Andrews)

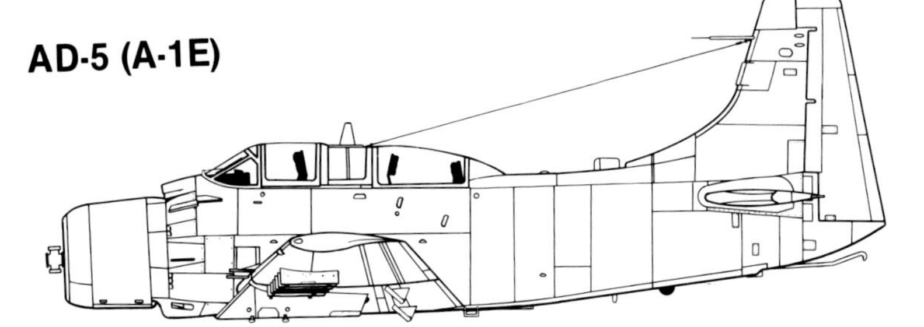

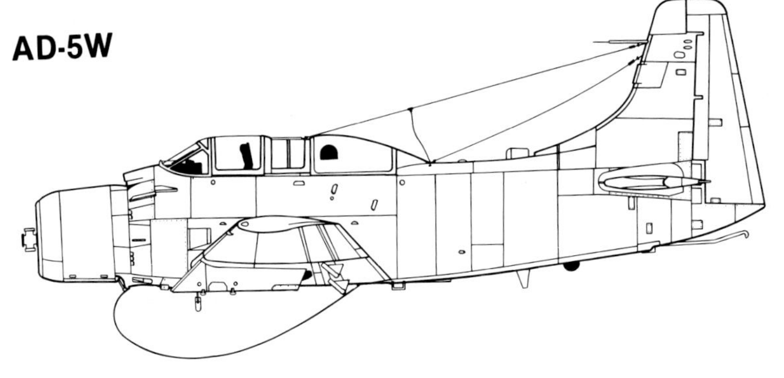

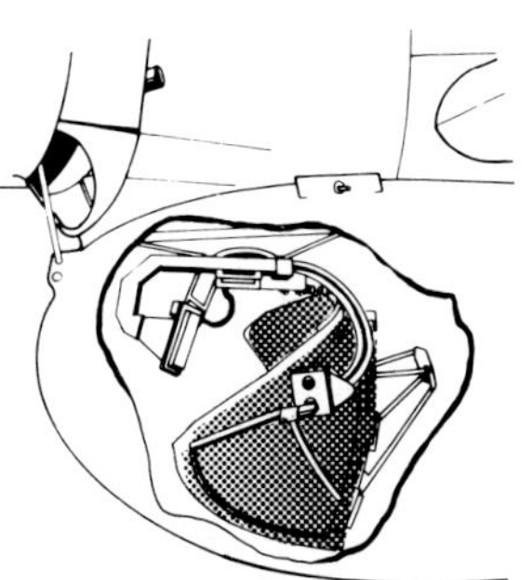

AD-5W Radar and Radome Arrangement

AD-5W (135187) of VC-11 carries White Modex 'ND'. June 1956. (National Archives)

AD-5S Search Light/ECM pod and pylon mount assembly

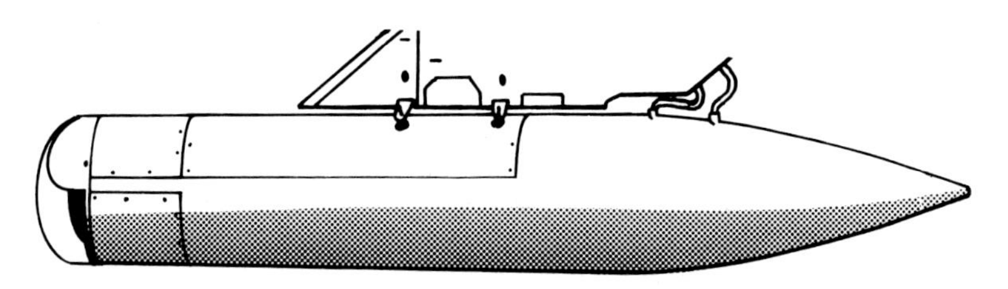

AD-5S (132479), a one-of-kind anti-submarine hunter equipped with Magnetic Anomaly Detection (MAD) system. Note the boom housing just beneath the rudder. The Skyraider submarine-hunter project was cancelled when the Grumman hunter-killer S2F-1 Tracker was accepted. El Segundo, CA. 4 June 1953. (via Hal Andrews)

A-1H (AD-6) (134530) of VA-165 makes a successful recovery, with hung-up ordnance, aboard Intrepid which was patrolling at 'Yankee Station' in the Gulf of Tonkin. September 1966. (USN via Walt Ohlirch)

AD-6 (A-1H) Skyraider

Produced concurrently with the two place AD-5, the AD-6 was basically a refined AD-4B Nuclear Bomber with the capability of carrying atomic stores. The "Able Dog Six" also had the narrow fuselage, small canopy and the smaller tail surfaces of the earlier Skyraiders, but with a strengthened center section and simplified electronics equipment. Instrumented for all-weather flight and low level bombing. The -6 was powered by a Wright R-3350-26WD producing 2700 hp providing a top speed of 285 knots, with a service ceiling of 28,500 feet and a combat range of 1,143 nautical miles. The pilot was provided added protection with the addition of armor-plating to both sides of the fuselage just below the cockpit and on the bottom of the fuselage. The side fuselage dive brakes deleted on the -5, remained on the -6 series. Provisions were made for one 300 gallon centerline fuel tank and two 150 gallon wing tanks in addition to the internal self-sealing 380 gallon main tank. Wing armament was two 20MM cannon in each wing. A unique feature for emergency bail out, was the installation of an extraction rocket that pulled the pilot clear of the cockpit. The AD-6 was the first "Able Dog" to be built without sub-variants.

Douglas produced seven hundred thirteen of this single place attack aircraft through August of 1956. The AD-6 was flown by the USN, USMC and USAF. During the mid-1960s AD-6s were made available to the VNAF.

In 1962 the AD-6 was redesignated to A-1H.

AD-6 (135315) of VA-45 comes across the ramp of Intrepid. February 1955. (National Archives)

AD-6 (134488) of VA-25 launches from USS Independence in July 1959. (Tom McManus)

AD-6 (134467) of VMA-332 seen flying high over the Everglades near NAS Miami, FL. March 1956. (USMC)

(Below) AD-6 (135357) of VA-42 bolters off the angled-deck of the USS Forrstal. March 1956. (National Archives)

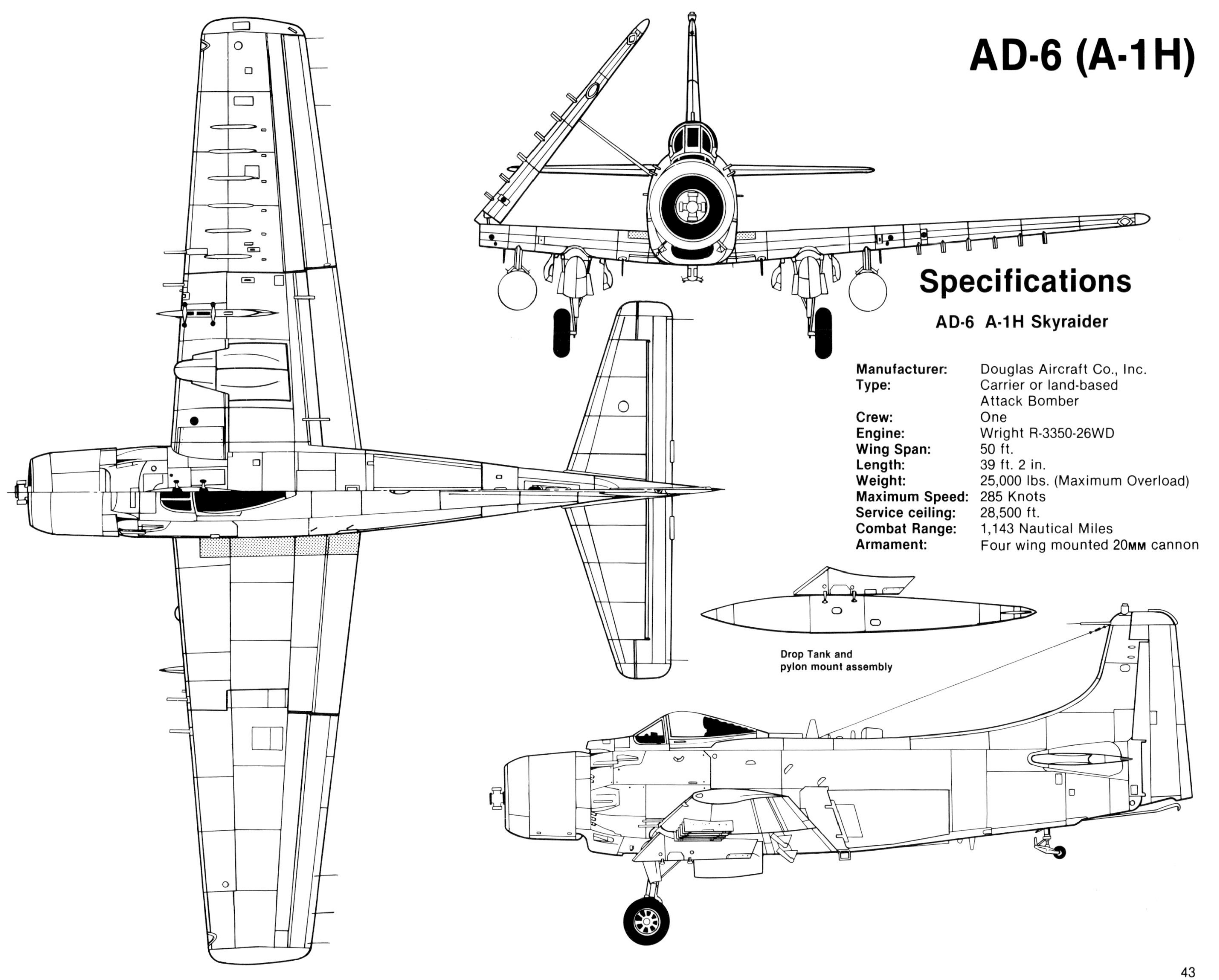
AD-6 (A-1H)
Specifications
AD-6 A-1H Skyraider
Manufacturer: Douglas Aircraft Co., Inc.
Type: Carrier or land-based Attack Bomber
Crew: One
Engine: Wright R-3350-26WD
Wing Span: 50 ft.
Length: 39 ft. 2 in.
Weight: 25,000 lbs. (Maximum Overload)
Maximum Speed: 285 Knots
Service ceiling: 28,500 ft.
Combat Range: 1,143 Nautical Miles
Armament: Four wing mounted 20MM cannon
Drop Tank and pylon mount assembly

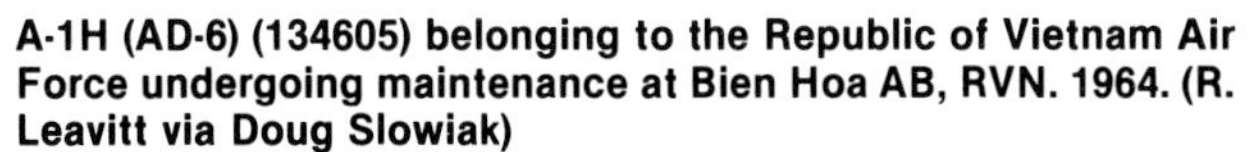

A-1H (AD-6) (134605) belonging to the Republic of Vietnam Air Force undergoing maintenance at Bien Hoa AB, RVN. 1964. (R. Leavitt via Doug Slowiak)

(Left) AD-6 (134564) of VA-196, pulling tight against the wire, recovers aboard USS Lexington. Note Red with Black trim on fin and rudder. July 1957. (National Archives)

(Right) AD-6 (137567) of VA-145 from USS Hornet, patroling over the Philippine Islands, February 1957. (National Archives)

Additional Armored Pilot Protection

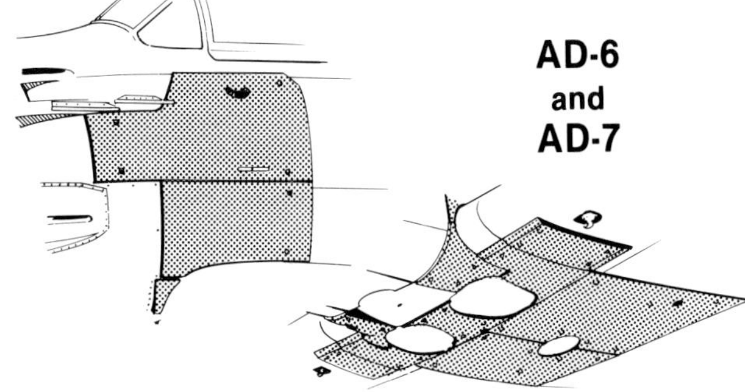
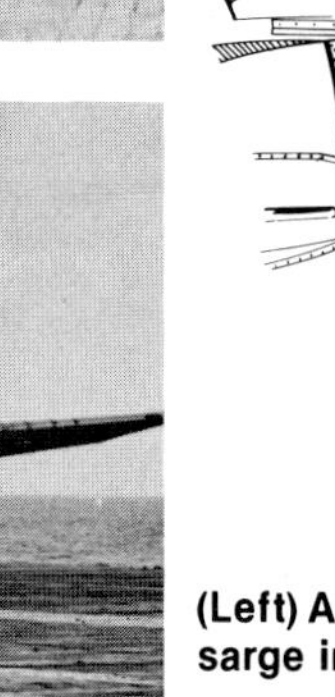

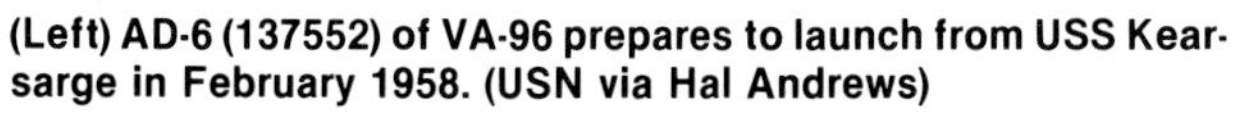

(Left) AD-6 (137552) of VA-96 prepares to launch from USS Kearsarge in February 1958. (USN via Hal Andrews)

(Right) AD-6 (135305) of FASRON-4 Detachment-A at NAS Miramar, CA. 1957. (Warren Bodie)

AD-6 (134608) of VMA-225 based at NAS Miami. Tail and wing tip trim is Dark Green stars on a White field with a Black band. Wilmington, NC. 1957. (Paul J. McDaniel)

AD-6 (139754) of VMA-331 carries the Black Modex 'VL'. The fin trim is Red. Note the 150 gallon wing tank. 1959. (USMC via W.F. Gemeinhardt)

(Left) A-1H (AD-6) (139746) of the Vietnamese Air Force seen in a colorful 'swept' Yellow and Black checkerboard fuselage trim. American trained Vietnamese pilots flew these Skyraiders. 27 September 1967. (via Peter Mancus)

(Right) AD-6 of VA-104 an instant before recovering aboard USS Leyte, 24 October 1955. (National Archives)

(Right) A-1H (AD-6) (134563) of VA-145 bellied in at NAS Miramar, CA. Note heavy oil staining on fuselage bottom. 23 January 1968. (USN via Walt Ohlrich)

(Left) A-1H (AD-6) (137545) of VA-196 in the markings of Air Station CO., Capt. Howard M. Avery. NAS Lemoore, CA. 25 April 1963. (USN via Bill Curry)

A-1H (AD-6) (139778) in the markings of VA-115, "The Arabs", from USS Kitty Hawk. Earlier markings are showing through the faded and peeling camouflage paint scheme. July 1966. (via Roger Besecker)

AD-6 (139799) of VA-35 aboard USS Saratoga while off the coast of Lebanon, July 1958. (USN via Hal Andrews)

A-1H (AD-6) (135332) of the 4407th CCTS, 1st SOW on the flightline at Hurlburt Field in Florida. Combat training for Vietnam was provided at this base. 1971. (Bob Esposito)

A-1H (AD-6) (135275) of VA-25 from USS Coral Sea heads inland for a strike on Vietnam. 1963. (via Roger Besecker)

AD-7 (A-1) Skyraider

AD-7 (142010) of VA-95, piloted by squadron CO., Cdr. Wright, has just released the cable after coming aboard USS Ranger. January 1960. (USN via Hal Andrews)

A-1J (AD-7) (142021) of VA-145 "Swordsmen", is fully loaded and on display at the Reno Air Races. 23 September 1966. (Author's Collection)

The final version of the Skyraider, the AD-7, was externally identical to the AD-6. Powered by the new Wright R-3350-26WB engine, top speed was 285 knots and combat range was 1128 nautical miles. The AD-7 had the strongest landing gear, as well as strengthened wing spars and wing fittings. Because the Navy needed additional fuel tankers, the AD-7 was ordered equipped with external refueling equipment. The program was so successfull that additional refueling kits were ordered for retro-fitting to the earlier AD-6s for the tanker role.

The Navy had originally planned to acquire 240 AD-7s, however, most of these were cancelled, with only 72 AD-7s being produced by Douglas. On 18 February 1957, an era came to an end, when the last piston engine Navy bomber rolled off the assembly line, an AD-7 (142081). A total of 3,180 Skyraiders had been produced.

In 1962 the AD-7 was redesignated A-1J.

AD-7 (A-1J)

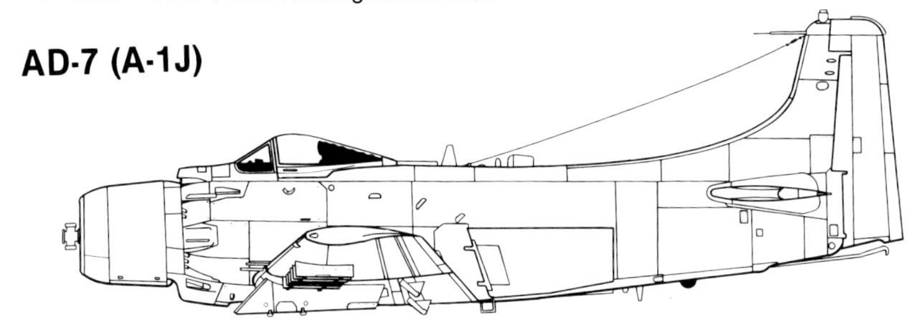

Airplanes BuNo. 139606 through 142081

1. Landing check list
1A. Marker beacon audio switch
2. Marker beacon light
3. Manifold pressure gauge
4. Deleted
5. Eight-day clock
6. Airspeed indicator
7. AN/APN-22 radar altimeter
8. LABS indicator light (above shield)
9. Deleted
10. Vertical gyro indicator
11. Gunsight
11A. LABS indicator
11B. Magnetic sump plugs warning light
12. Deleted
13. Deleted
14. Standby compass
14A. LABS control panel
15. Windshield degreaser
16. Fuel quantity test switch
17. Fuel quantity indicator
18. Fuel pressure warning light
19. Take-off check list
20. OAT-carburetor air temp. indicator
21. Outside air temperature switch
21A. Torque pressure gauge
22. Deleted
22A. ID-249/ARN course indicator
23. Generator warning light
24. Accelerometer
25. Engine gauge unit
26. Cylinder head temperature indicator
27. ID-250/ARN course indicator
28. Rate-of-climb indicator
28A. Deleted
28B. ID-310/ARN range indicator
29. Rudder pedal adjustment crank
29A. P-1 autopilot gyro horizon
30. Turn-and-bank indicator
30A. Chartboard
31. Altimeter
32. Tachometer
32A. Water injection switch
33. Wheels and flaps position indicator
34. Ignition switch
35. Dive check list

A-1J (AD-7) (142074) of VA-145, returning from patrol prepares to land aboard USS Constellation. The 'Swordsmen' pulled combat duty in Vietnam. 20 June 1963. (USN via Bill Curry)

AD-7 (142015) of VA-122, a training squadron based at NAS Lemoore, CA., shows the underwing rack detail to good advantage. 1960. (USN via Bill Curry)

A-1J (AD-7) (142076) of 1st Special Operations Squadron (SOS) 56th Special Operations Wing (SOW). Note the deletion of the national insignia. This fully-loaded Skyraider is seen near Laos. C. 1966. (via Don Jay)

A2D-1 Skyshark

Under the designation A2D-1 Skyshark, the AD-3 airframe was mated to an Allison T-40 turboprop engine turning two massive Aeroproducts contra-rotating propellers. The T-40 was essentially two side-by-side turbojet engines mounted through gearing to the propeller shafts. Additional power was developed from the engines' jet thrust vented through exhaust ports on each side of the fuselage just behind the wing root. To conserve fuel during flight, one of the two engines could be shut down. The Skyshark was equipped with an ejection seat for pilot escape. Six examples were built and tested, but difficulties in engine development, reduction gearing and the counter-rotating props caused the projects termination.

A2D-1 (125482) at the Naval Air Test Center at Patuxent River, MD. This Skyshark was stricken from the Navy inventory in February 1954. (via Pete Bowers)

The Walk Around Series

Each book provides an in-depth look at the subject, inside and out, using color and black and white photos, illustrations, and line art. 40 pages of color, 40 pages of black and white.

5504 F4F Wildcat

5507 P-51D Mustang

5508 P-40 Warhawk

5509 F6F Hellcat

5510 Fw 190D

5511 P-47 Thunderbolt

5512 B-25 Mitchell

5513 Allison-Engined Mustangs